Essentials of
Biostatistics Workbook

Statistical Computing
Using Excel

Lisa M. Sullivan, PhD

Chair, Department of Biostatistics
Boston University School of Public Health,
Boston, Massachusetts

JONES AND BARTLETT PUBLISHERS

Sudbury, Massachusetts

BOSTON   TORONTO   LONDON   SINGAPORE

World Headquarters

Jones and Bartlett Publishers
40 Tall Pine Drive
Sudbury, MA 01776
978-443-5000
info@jbpub.com
www.jbpub.com

Jones and Bartlett Publishers
Canada
6339 Ormindale Way
Mississauga, Ontario
L5V 1J2
Canada

Jones and Bartlett Publishers
International
Barb House, Barb Mews
London W6 7PA
United Kingdom

Jones and Bartlett's books and products are available through most bookstores and online booksellers. To contact Jones and Bartlett Publishers directly, call 800-832-0034, fax 978-443-8000, or visit our website www.jbpub.com.

Substantial discounts on bulk quantities of Jones and Bartlett's publications are available to corporations, professional associations, and other qualified organizations. For details and specific discount information, contact the special sales department at Jones and Bartlett via the above contact information or send an email to specialsales@jbpub.com.

This publication is designed to provide accurate and authoritative information in regard to the Subject Matter covered. It is sold with the understanding that the publisher is not engaged in rendering legal, accounting, or other professional service. If legal advice or other expert assistance is required, the service of a competent professional person should be sought.

Production Credits
Publisher: Michael Brown
Associate Editor: Katey Birtcher
Production Director: Amy Rose
Production Editor: Tracey Chapman
Marketing Manager: Sophie Fleck
Manufacturing Buyer: Therese Connell
Composition: Publishers' Design and Production Services, Inc.
Cover Design: Kristin E. Ohlin
Cover Image: © Digital Vision/Getty Images
Printing and Binding: Courier Stoughton
Cover Printing: Courier Stoughton

6048
Printed in the United States of America
12 11 10 09 08   10 9 8 7 6 5 4 3 2

Table of Contents

CHAPTER 1

Basics

In this workbook, we describe how Microsoft Excel can be used to perform the statistical computations and analyses described in the textbook. Excel is a popular program, often used for organizing and summarizing numerical or financial information. It has substantial graphing capabilities and a statistical analysis module that is designed to perform a number of statistical analyses. One of the primary reasons we use Excel is its accessibility. Whereas other statistical packages (e.g., SAS, SPSS, and S-Plus) offer more advanced analytic techniques and procedures, Excel is suitable for the introductory procedures we present here.[1-3] In fact, Excel offers many more applications than those we will present in this workbook. We will focus on the concepts and procedures discussed in the textbook. Readers interested in broader applications of Excel should see Dretzke.[4] Before we proceed with specific analyses, we first present some basic terminology and general procedures to get started.

1.1   WORKBOOKS AND WORKSHEETS

Excel files are also called workbooks. A *workbook* is a set of worksheets, where each *worksheet* can be thought of as a table or grid of rows and columns. When we open the Excel program, a workbook with three blank worksheets is presented (this is the default, or preset starting point). Excel calls the new workbook *Book1*. The name can be changed when the workbook is saved (see Section 1.4 for details). The three worksheets are called *Sheet1*, *Sheet2*, and *Sheet3*. The names of the worksheets can also be changed. When Excel is opened, *Sheet1* is shown on the screen and it looks like an empty grid of rows and columns; a sample is shown in Figure 1-1. The columns of the worksheet are labeled with letters (A, B, C,

and so on) and the rows of the worksheet are numbered. The workbook name appears in the top-left corner *(Book1)*, and the tabs along the bottom of the screen show the worksheet names.

It is useful to rename the worksheets to reflect the information stored in each. For example, we will rename *Sheet1* as *Data*. This can be done using the "Format" option along the top menu bar. Under the "Format" option, we choose the "Sheet" and "Rename" options, respectively (see Figure 1-2). Once we choose the "Rename" option, Excel places the cursor on the worksheet name at the bottom of the screen (*Sheet1* in this case), where we can enter the new name.

1.2   CELL ADDRESSES

A worksheet can be thought of as a set of cells. Each *cell* is defined by a specific column and row. When we first open Excel, the cursor appears in the top-left cell, making that the current or active cell. Notice in Figure 1-1 and Figure 1-2 that the top-left cell is outlined in a bold black line. The column and row make up the cell's address. The top-left cell's address is A1. As we move the cursor around the worksheet into different cells, the address of the current or active cell is shown just below the menu bars in the top-left portion of the screen.

1.3   ENTERING AND EDITING DATA

For statistical analysis, we enter data into the cells of the Excel worksheet. Once the data are entered, we can manipulate the values and perform statistical analyses. Example 1.1 contains data from a small study that we will use to illustrate entering and manipulating data.

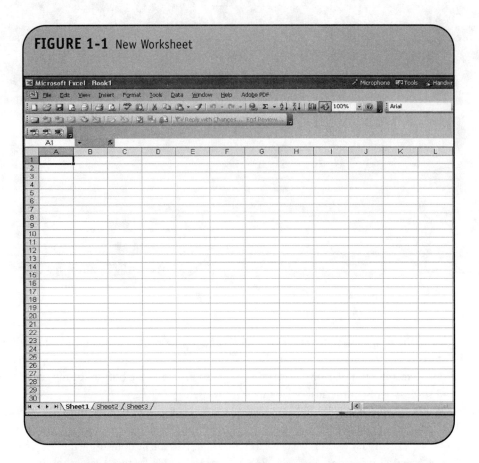

FIGURE 1-1 New Worksheet

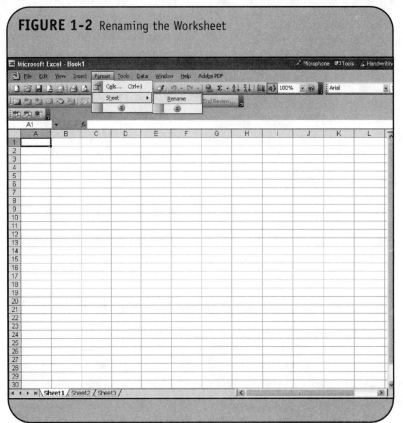

FIGURE 1-2 Renaming the Worksheet

TABLE 1-1 Data from Study of 5 Participants

Subject Identification Number	Age	Gender	Weight (lb)	Height (in)
1	24	F	125	63
2	21	F	140	68
3	32	M	165	68
4	27	M	170	72
5	25	M	195	71

Example 1.1. Suppose we have a sample of $n = 5$ partici-pants and on each participant we measure age, gender, weight, and height. We also assign each participant a unique identification number (shown in the first column of Table 1-1). The identification numbers are not used in statistical analysis but instead to keep track of data measured in the same participant. The data are shown in Table 1-1.

In Excel, we use the columns to hold different variables (e.g., identification number, age, gender, weight, and height)

and the rows to hold observations measured in different participants. We use the first row for the variable names—this is important as the variable names will show on the output, making for easier interpretation. The data shown in Table 1-1 are entered into Excel by moving the cursor around the worksheet. Figure 1-3 shows the data entered into the worksheet we named *Data*. Notice that the variable names are contained in row 1 and the data measured on the five participants are shown in row 2 through row 6. There is

FIGURE 1-3 Study Data Entered into Excel Worksheet

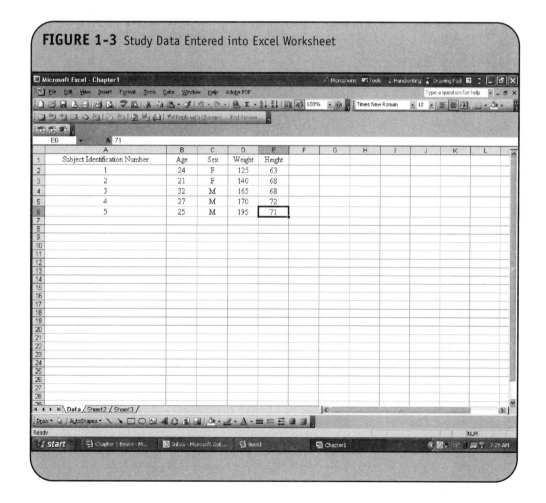

no restriction on the format or length of variable names. However, it can be easier to work with shorter names, simply for viewing the names and data on the worksheet. It is important to choose informative names that reflect the information entered.

In Figure 1-3, the current or active cell is E6. The cell name is shown just below the menu bar in the top-left portion of the screen. The contents of the cell (71 in the example) are shown just to the right of the active cell's address. Once data are entered, we can change or modify entries simply by retyping over the contents of the current cell or by typing into the top row where the active cell's contents are shown (see Figure 1-3). We can move from cell to cell in the worksheet by moving the mouse or by using the arrow keys on the keyboard.

There are some instances where the same data are repeated. In Example 1.1, there are two women and three men. Suppose we enter the gender of Participant 1 (i.e., participant with identification number 1 whose data are in row 2 of the *Data* worksheet) into the C2 cell as "F". Rather than entering the gender of Participant 2 into cell C3 directly, we can copy the data from the C2 cell. First, we make the C2 cell the active cell by moving the cursor to that cell. We then click on the "Copy" icon on the menu bar. To let us know that the contents of the active cell have been copied, Excel shows the borders of the cell with a bold flashing dotted line (as opposed to a bold solid line). We then move the cursor to the destination cell (e.g., C3) and click on the "Paste" icon. The contents of cell C2 are copied and pasted into cell C3. The same idea can be used to copy the contents of one cell to several cells. Suppose we enter the gender of Participant 3 into cell C4 as "M" and want to copy the contents of cell C4 in to cells C5 and C6. We make cell C4 the active cell and click on the "Copy" icon. We then highlight the destination cells—in this case, cells C5 and C6 simultaneously. To do this, we place our cursor on cell C5 (the top or first cell in the range) and, holding the left mouse key down, we drag the cursor to cell C6. This highlights both cells C5 and C6. We then hit the "Paste" icon and the contents of cell C4 are copied into cells C5 and C6.

To insert a row into a worksheet, we use the "Insert/Row" command on the menu bar. Once we select the "Insert/Row" option, a row is inserted above the active cell. The same approach can be taken to insert a column. Selecting the "Insert/Column" option from the menu bar inserts a column to the left of the active cell.

For reporting purposes, we often want to format data or results for a consistent presentation. The "Format" option on the main menu bar can be used to format the contents of any cell or cells in a worksheet. For example, we entered weights in pounds, as shown into our *Data* worksheet:

Weight
125
140
165
170
195

Suppose that weights were actually measured to the nearest hundredths place and the data were entered as:

Weight
125.45
140.05
165.16
170.39
195.47

Suppose that we want to present the weights to the nearest tenths place (i.e., round the weights to one decimal place). This can be performed using the "Format" option on the main menu bar. We first highlight the range of cells we want to format (in our example, cells D2 through D6). We then click on the "Format/Cells" option. This is shown in Figure 1-4.

Choosing the "Format/Cells" option brings up the dialog box shown in Figure 1-5, where we can specify the format we want for the selected cells. In Figure 1-5, we select the "Number" format (from the category list on the left side of the dialog box) and specify "1" decimal place. Once we click "OK," the weights in the worksheet change to the following:

Weight
125.5
140.1
165.2
170.4
195.5

The format option is particularly useful for formatting results. For example, when we compute the mean or standard deviation of a sample, Excel carries more decimal places than we will want to present. Recall that as a general rule, we report summary statistics that have one more decimal place than the raw data. Reporting too many decimal places implies a false level of precision. We will illustrate how to format results in Chapter 4 through Chapter 9 of the Excel Workbook.

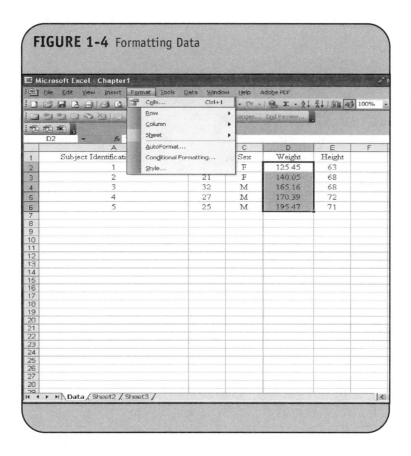

FIGURE 1-4 Formatting Data

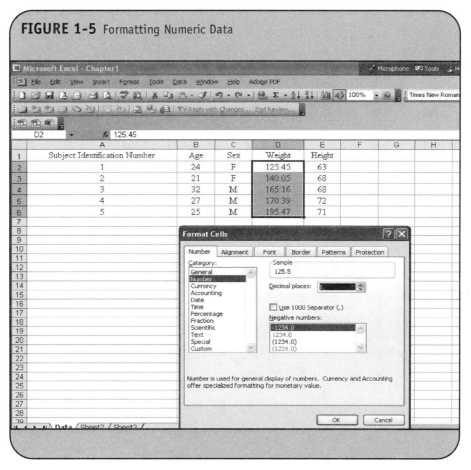

FIGURE 1-5 Formatting Numeric Data

1.4   SAVING FILES

The "File/Save As" option is used to save a workbook (and its associated worksheets). Figure 1-6 shows the commands. After selecting the "File/Save As" option, Excel prompts us to enter a file name to store the workbook. Once a workbook is saved as a file, we can open it using the "File/Open" option for further use.

1.5   PRACTICE PROBLEMS

1. Use Excel to create a worksheet with the data shown in Table 1-2. The data were presented in Table 4-13 in the textbook and were measured in a subsample of $n = 10$ participants who attended the seventh examination of the Framingham Offspring Study. Place the variable names in the first row of the worksheet.

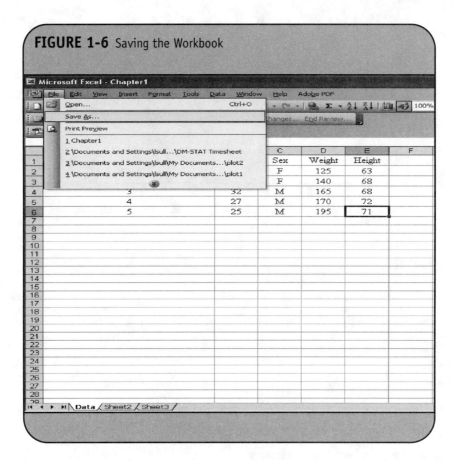

FIGURE 1-6 Saving the Workbook

TABLE 1-2 Data for Practice Problem 1

Participant ID	Systolic Blood Pressure	Diastolic Blood Pressure	Total Serum Cholesterol	Weight (lb)	Height (in)
1	141	76	199	138	63.00
2	119	64	150	183	69.75
3	122	62	227	153	65.75
4	127	81	227	178	70.00
5	125	70	163	161	70.50
6	123	72	210	206	70.00
7	105	81	205	235	72.00
8	113	63	275	151	60.75
9	106	67	208	213	69.00
10	131	77	159	142	61.00

2. Rename the worksheet with the data from Problem 1 as *Data*.

3. Save the Excel workbook as a file.

REFERENCES

1. SAS Version 9.1$^{©}$ 2002–2003 by SAS Institute Inc., Cary, NC.
2. SPSS® Version 15.0$^{©}$ 2006 by SPSS Inc., Chicago, IL.
3. S-PLUS Version 7.0$^{©}$ 1999–2006 by Insightful Corp., Seattle, WA.
4. Dretzke, B.J. *Statistics with Microsoft® Excel* (3rd ed). Upper Saddle River, NJ: Pearson Prentice Hall, 2005.

CHAPTER 2

Formulas, Functions, and the Data Analysis ToolPak

Once data are entered into an Excel worksheet, we can create formulas and functions to organize, manipulate, and analyze the data. For example, Excel can be used to create new variables from existing variables (e.g., to convert variables from one scale of measurement to another, to standardize variables into z scores, or to create new variables from those that are measured directly), or to compute summary statistics (e.g., the mean, standard deviation, or median of a dataset, the minimum or maximum values).

2.1 BASIC MATHEMATICAL OPERATIONS

Basic mathematical operations are performed in Excel as they are on a calculator or in other statistical computing packages. In Excel, the following operations are implemented with the respective operators shown in Table 2-1.

The order of operations is exponentiation, multiplication and division, and then addition and subtraction. To implement mathematical operations, we "program" specific operations into the cells of a worksheet. For example, we can use these operations to convert variables measured on one scale to another or to create new variables from existing variables.

In Example 1.1 of the Excel workbook, we presented data on $n = 5$ participants. We measured age (in years), gender (male/female), weight (in pounds), and height (in inches). The data for Participant 1 are shown in Table 2-2. Using Excel, we could convert age measured in years to age in months by multiplying age in years by 12 (e.g., Age_months = Age_years $\times$ 12). We could also convert weight in pounds to weight in kilograms using Weight_kilograms = Weight_pounds/0.4636. Excel can be used to make these transformations easily. We will illustrate how this is done in Section 2.2.

Example 2.1. Consider a study designed to assess the impact of a medication designed to lower systolic blood pressure. Suppose we measure each participant's baseline systolic blood pressure (SBP) and their systolic blood pressure after 6 months on treatment. The data on $n = 3$ participants are entered into Excel and shown in Figure 2-1.

Notice that the distinct variables (e.g., ID, baseline, and 6-month systolic blood pressures) are shown in the columns and data for each participant are shown in the rows of the worksheet. To analyze these data, we use methods for dependent, matched, or paired samples and focus specifically on differences in blood pressures. For each participant, we need to first compute the differences. We can take differences as

$$\text{Difference} = 6 \text{ Month SBP} - \text{Baseline SBP}$$

TABLE 2-1 Mathematical Operators in Excel

Operation	Operator
Multiplication	*
Division	/
Addition	+
Subtraction	-
Exponentiation	^

TABLE 2-2 Participant Data

Subject Identification Number	Age	Gender	Weight (lb)	Height (in)
1	24	F	125	63

2.2   RELATIVE AND ABSOLUTE CELL REFERENCES

The operations described in Section 2.1 can be implemented in Excel by "programming" the operations into cells in the Excel worksheet. The programming amounts to specifying equations in Excel to perform the desired operations. We are essentially creating new variables as functions of existing variables using specific operations (e.g., converting from one scale to another, creating difference scores). To implement these operations, we first choose a column location for the new variable and specify a name for the new variable. The new variable name is placed in the first row of the worksheet along with the other variable names. We then input the operation or formula to create the new variable. In Excel, these operations are indicated by an equals sign ("="). When Excel sees an equals sign in a cell, it is expecting a formula to follow.

The formula is implemented to produce the desired result, which is placed into that cell. Figure 2-2 shows the data from Example 1.1 of the Excel workbook in a worksheet.

Suppose we want to create a new variable, age in months, and we label it "Age, months." We first choose a location for the variable. Suppose we want to place the new variable in column F of the worksheet. We enter the new name into row 1 of column F, as shown in Figure 2-2. Age in months is computed by multiplying age in years (which is contained in column B) by 12. Specifically, the formula to create "Age, months" is "Age (in years)" × 12. This formula is entered into cell F2 as "=B2*12". In this formula, B2 represents the address of the cell containing the age in years for Participant 1. Once the formula is entered, Excel takes the value from B2 (24 years) and multiplies it by 12. The result (288) is placed into cell F2.

To compute this operation for each participant, we copy the formula in cell F2 and paste it into cell F3 through cell F6. This is done by making F2 the active cell and clicking the "Copy" icon. The border of cell F2 is shown in a bold, flashing dotted line. We next highlight cell F3 through cell F6 and click the "Paste" icon. The formula is copied from cell F2 into cell F3 through cell F6. Excel automatically updates the cell referencing

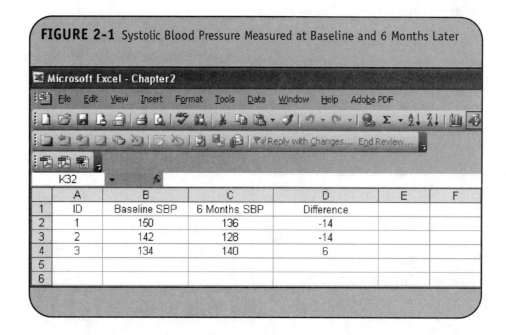

FIGURE 2-1 Systolic Blood Pressure Measured at Baseline and 6 Months Later

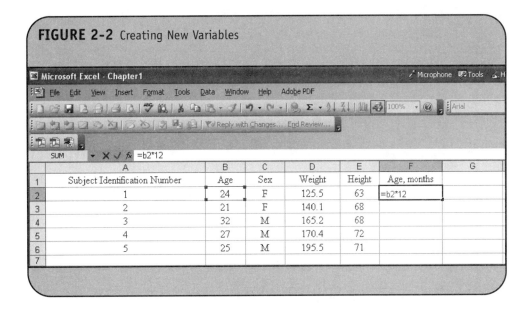

FIGURE 2-2 Creating New Variables

	A	B	C	D	E	F	G
1	Subject Identification Number	Age	Sex	Weight	Height	Age, months	
2	1	24	F	125.5	63	=b2*12	
3	2	21	F	140.1	68		
4	3	32	M	165.2	68		
5	4	27	M	170.4	72		
6	5	25	M	195.5	71		
7							

(i.e., the locations of the cells that contain the ages in years for each participant). Specifically, when we enter the formula to compute age in months for Participant 1 into F2, we specify that Excel should take the data in cell B2 and multiply it by 12. We want to do the same for the remaining participants. For each participant, we want to multiply their age in years by 12. When we copy and paste the formula from cell F2 into cell F3 through cell F6, Excel updates the cell references as shown in Figure 2-3.

Excel automatically updates the formula to compute age in months for Participant 2 through Participant 5 by updating the cell references (i.e., B3 through B6). These references are called *relative cell references.* The formula to compute age in months for each participant uses the relevant information, the age in years for that participant, contained in column B.

Consider again the data in Example 2.1 shown in Figure 2-1. Suppose we now want to create the difference variable. Figure 2-4 shows the new variable (column D) and the formula to compute it in cell D2. The difference score is computed by subtracting the baseline SBP (column B) from the SBP measured at 6 months (column C). The formula for

FIGURE 2-3 Using Relative Cell References

	A	B	C	D	E	F	G
1	Subject Identification Number	Age	Sex	Weight	Height	Age, months	
2	1	24	F	125	63	=B2*12	
3	2	21	F	140	68	=B3*12	
4	3	32	M	165	68	=B4*12	
5	4	27	M	170	72	=B5*12	
6	5	25	M	195	71	=B6*12	
7							
8							

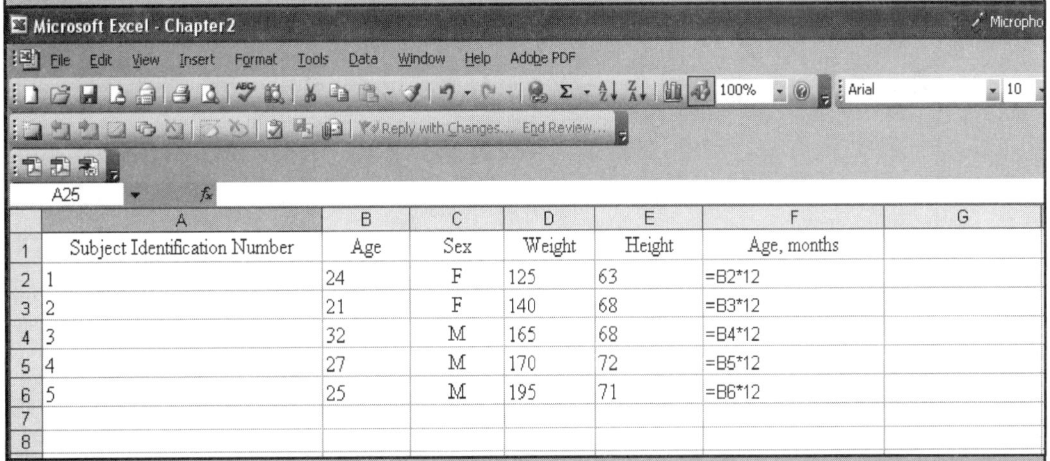

FIGURE 2-4 Computing Differences

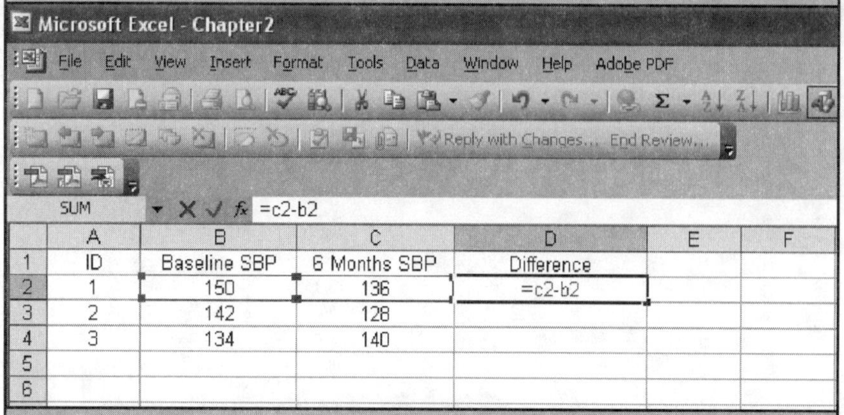

Participant 1 is "=C2−B2". If we copy the contents of cell D2 into cell D3 and cell D4, Excel automatically updates the cell referencing. The formulas are "=C3−B3" and "=C4−B4", respectively. Once the formulas are entered, Excel computes the differences and the results are shown in Figure 2-5.

Example 2.2. Suppose we measure the lengths (in centimeters) of $n = 6$ infant boys who are 12 months of age. Suppose we want to standardize the lengths by subtracting the mean and dividing by the standard deviation. The mean length for 12-month-old boys is reported as 75 centimeters and the standard deviation is reported as 2.1 centimeters. The data are entered into an Excel worksheet as shown in Figure 2-6.

The lengths in centimeters are shown in column A. We standardize the lengths by subtracting the mean and dividing by the standard deviation as $Z = (\text{Length} − 75)/2.1$. To create the new variable Z, we enter the formula as shown in Figure 2-7. If we copy the formula from cell B2 into cell B3 through cell B7, Excel updates the cell references to use the lengths in centimeters in cell A3 through cell A7, respectively.

There is a second way to perform the standardization. Suppose we enter the data into an Excel worksheet as shown in Figure 2-8. The mean and standard deviation are now shown in cell B9 and cell B10, respectively. We again create Z scores by

FIGURE 2-5 Difference Scores

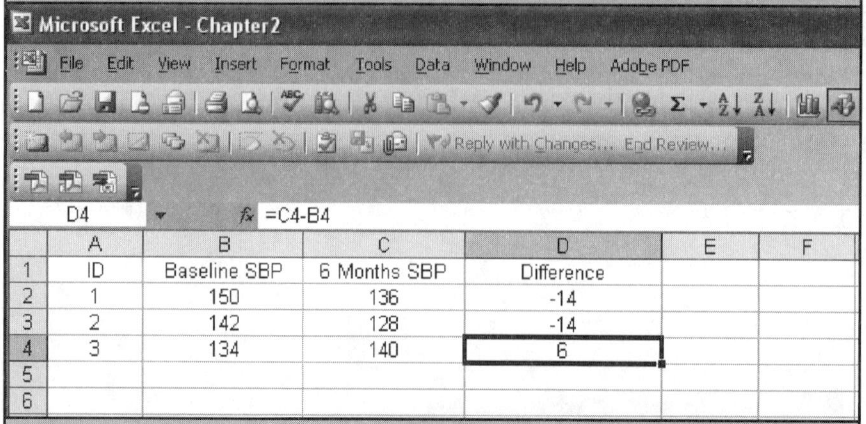

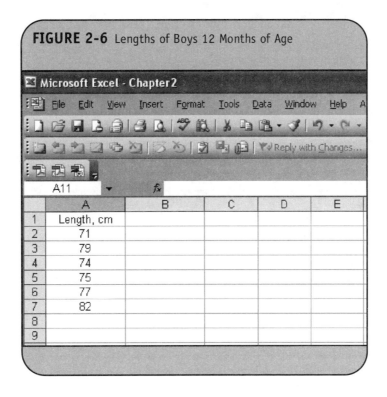

FIGURE 2-6 Lengths of Boys 12 Months of Age

	A	B	C	D	E
1	Length, cm				
2	71				
3	79				
4	74				
5	75				
6	77				
7	82				
8					
9					

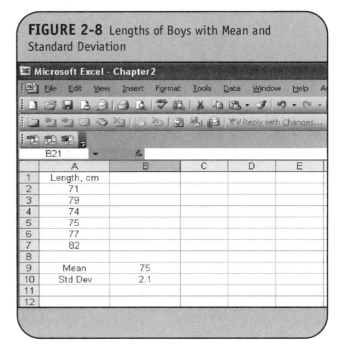

FIGURE 2-7 Standardizing the Lengths

	A	B	C	D	E
1	Length, cm	Z			
2	71	=(A2-75)/2.1			
3	79				
4	74				
5	75				
6	77				
7	82				
8					
9					
10					

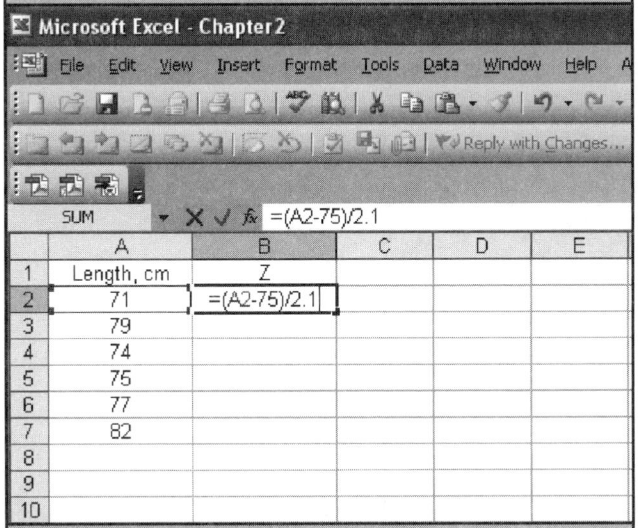

FIGURE 2-8 Lengths of Boys with Mean and Standard Deviation

	A	B	C	D	E
1	Length, cm				
2	71				
3	79				
4	74				
5	75				
6	77				
7	82				
8					
9	Mean	75			
10	Std Dev	2.1			
11					
12					

taking each length in column A, subtracting the mean of 75 and dividing by the standard deviation of 2.1. What we do here is refer Excel to the cells containing the mean and standard deviation (i.e., cell B9 and cell B10) in the worksheet. If we again place the *Z* scores in column B, the formula entered in cell B2 is "=(A2−$B$9)/$B$10". A dollar sign before a column or row in a cell address freezes or fixes that column or row (as opposed to allowing Excel to update a relative address as per the previous examples). In this example, we are fixing both the columns and rows of the addresses of the mean and standard deviation. These are called *absolute cell references*. Figure 2-9 displays the formulas that are copied into cell B3 through cell B7; notice that the cell addresses for the mean and standard deviation do not change from cell to cell.

When we enter the formulas, the results are shown in column B. Both of the methods illustrated in Figure 2-7 and Figure 2-9 produce the results shown in Figure 2-10. The boy of length 71 cm is 1.9 standard deviations below the mean, whereas the boy of length 79 cm is 1.9 standard deviations above the mean. For presentation purposes, we can format the cells in column B (using the "Format/Cells" option, see Figure 1-4 and Figure 1-5) to two decimal places.

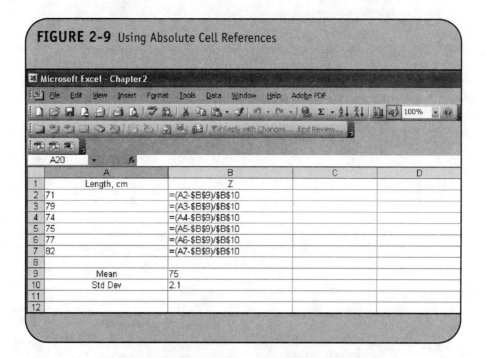

FIGURE 2-9 Using Absolute Cell References

	A	B	C	D
1	Length, cm	Z		
2	71	=(A2-$B$9)/$B$10		
3	79	=(A3-$B$9)/$B$10		
4	74	=(A4-$B$9)/$B$10		
5	75	=(A5-$B$9)/$B$10		
6	77	=(A6-$B$9)/$B$10		
7	82	=(A7-$B$9)/$B$10		
8				
9	Mean	75		
10	Std Dev	2.1		
11				
12				

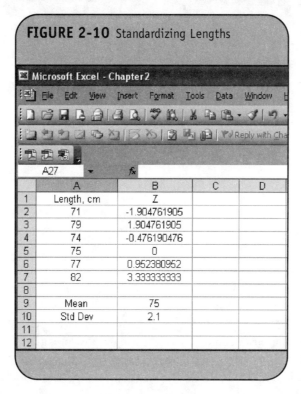

FIGURE 2-10 Standardizing Lengths

	A	B	C	D
1	Length, cm	Z		
2	71	-1.904761905		
3	79	1.904761905		
4	74	-0.476190476		
5	75	0		
6	77	0.952380952		
7	82	3.333333333		
8				
9	Mean	75		
10	Std Dev	2.1		
11				
12				

2.3 CREATING FORMULAS AND FUNCTIONS

We now describe how Excel is used to compute summary statistics (e.g., $\overline{X}$, s, median) using formulas and functions.

Example 2.3. In many studies of cardiovascular disease (e.g., the Framingham Heart Study), body mass index is assessed as a risk factor. Body mass index (BMI) is defined as

$$\text{BMI} = \text{weight}_{\text{kilograms}} \,/\, \text{height}_{\text{meters}}{}^{2}$$

Often weights are measured in pounds and heights in inches. Thus, the observed measurements must be converted to kilograms and meters, respectively, and then divided to produce BMI scores. In Example 1.1 of the Excel Workbook, we measured weight in pounds and height in inches in $n = 5$ participants. Suppose we now want to create a BMI for each participant. The conversion from pounds to kilograms is 1 pound = 0.4536 kilograms, and the conversion from inches to meters is 1 inch = 0.0254 meters. The formula to compute BMI from weight in pounds and height in inches is

$$\text{BMI} = \frac{\text{weight}_{\text{pounds}} \times 0.4536}{(\text{height}_{\text{inches}} \times 0.0254)^2}$$

Figure 2-11 shows the computation of BMI. The formula in cell H2 can be copied to cell H3 through cell H6 to compute BMI for each participant. Notice the power operator "^2", used to square the height in the denominator of the formula. Once the formula is copied, the BMI scores are computed as shown in Figure 2-12. Before we compute summary statistics on the BMI data, we first use the "Format/Cells" option to format the BMIs to two decimal places (Figure 2-13).

Excel has a number of functions and formulas that can be used to summarize and analyze data. We now use Excel to compute the sample mean BMI (i.e., $\overline{X} = \Sigma X / n$) using these functions. We first sum the BMI scores and place the sum in cell H8. This is done with the SUM function. In cell H8, we enter the formula "=SUM(H2:H6)". The SUM function sums the data in the cells listed in the range shown in parentheses. In this example, we want to sum the data in cell H2 through cell H6. We then compute the sample size using the COUNT function and place the sample size into cell H9. In cell H9, we enter the formula "=COUNT(H2:H6)". The COUNT function tallies the number of cells with non-missing data. The sample mean is computed by dividing the sum by the sample size, and we place the sample mean into cell H10. Specifically, in cell H10 we enter the formula "=H8/H9". We use column G for labels (Figure 2-13).

Suppose we now wish to compute the standard deviation of BMI (i.e., $s = \sqrt{\frac{\Sigma(X-\overline{X})^2}{n-1}}$). We need to first subtract the mean BMI (in cell H10) from each BMI and square the difference. We place the squared differences in column I, and the formula entered in cell I2 is "=(H2−$H$10)^2". We then sum the squared differences using the SUM function (i.e., "=SUM(I2:I6)") and place the result in cell I8. The variance is computed by dividing the sum of the squared differences by

FIGURE 2-11 Computing BMI From Height and Weight

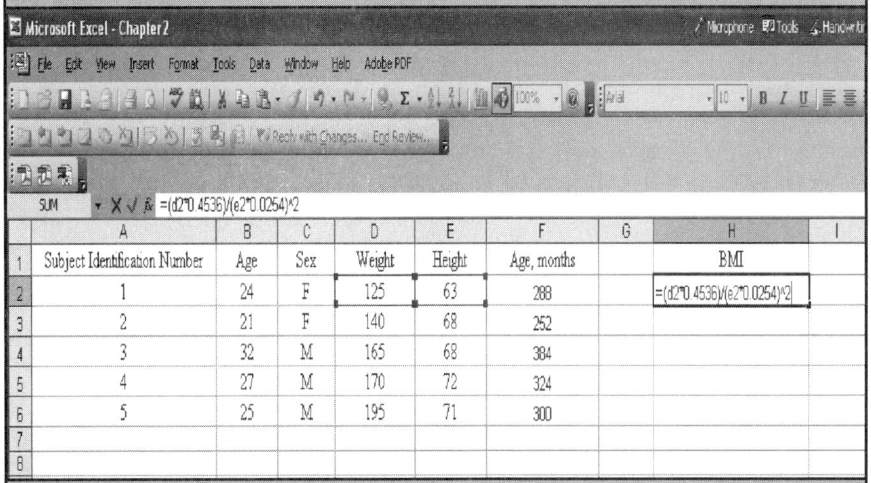

	A	B	C	D	E	F	G	H	I
1	Subject Identification Number	Age	Sex	Weight	Height	Age, months		BMI	
2	1	24	F	125	63	288		=(d2*0.4536)/(e2*0.0254)^2	
3	2	21	F	140	68	252			
4	3	32	M	165	68	384			
5	4	27	M	170	72	324			
6	5	25	M	195	71	300			
7									
8									

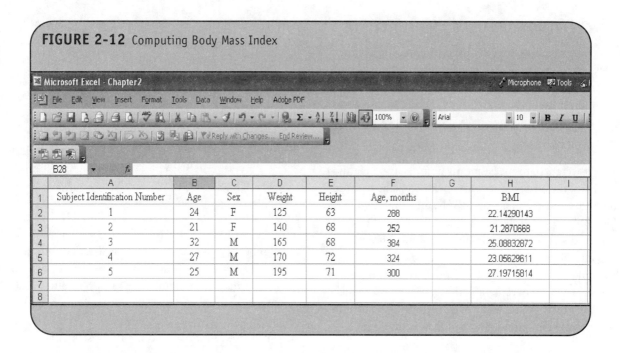

FIGURE 2-12 Computing Body Mass Index

FIGURE 2-13 Computing the Sample Mean

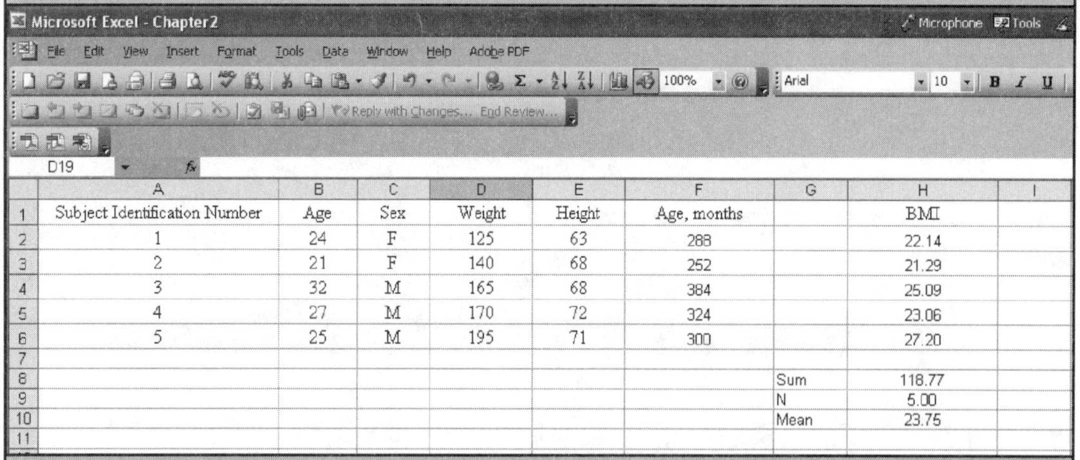

$(n-1)$. We compute the variance in cell I11 as "=I8/(H9−1)". The standard deviation is then computed as "=SQRT(I11)". Figure 2-14 displays the results.

Like many statistical computing packages, there are several ways to compute summary statistics in Excel. One way is to use the mathematical operations to program the formulas. A second method is to use one of Excel's many built-in functions that directly compute summary statistics on a continuous variable. For example, Excel has an AVERAGE function that computes a mean. First, we select a cell for the result. Suppose we wish to compute the mean age for the data shown in Figure 2-14, and we want to place the mean age in cell B8. We enter the following into cell B8: "=AVERAGE(B2:B6)". Once the formula is entered, the mean of the observations contained in cell B2 through cell B6 is computed and placed in cell B8. The AVERAGE function sums the data specified in parentheses

FIGURE 2-14 Computing the Sample Variance and Sample Standard Deviation

	A	B	C	D	E	F	G	H	I	J
1	Subject Identification Number	Age	Sex	Weight	Height	Age, months		BMI	(BMI-Mean BMI)^2	
2	1	24	F	125	63	288		22.14	2.60	
3	2	21	F	140	68	252		21.29	6.09	
4	3	32	M	165	68	384		25.09	1.78	
5	4	27	M	170	72	324		23.06	0.49	
6	5	25	M	195	71	300		27.20	11.85	
7										
8							Sum	118.77	22.80	
9							N	5.00		
10							Mean	23.75		
11								Variance	5.70	
12								Std Dev	2.39	
13										

(in the worksheet, the age data are in cell B2 through cell B6) and divides by the sample size (i.e., the total number of non-missing values). There are other functions available in Excel that are useful for computing summary statistics; these are discussed in Chapter 4 of the Excel workbook.

A third option for computing summary statistics is through the Excel Data Analysis ToolPak. The ToolPak offers a number of modules designed to perform various statistical analyses. We will introduce the ToolPak here and use it extensively in Chapter 4 through Chapter 9 of the Excel workbook to perform statistical analysis.

2.4 THE DATA ANALYSIS TOOLPAK

The Excel Data Analysis ToolPak is an additional (or add-in) module that must be loaded either at the time of installation of Excel or at a later date. If the ToolPak was loaded at installation, it will be available as an option on the "Tools" menu (Figure 2-15).

If the Data Analysis ToolPak is not available, it can be loaded at any time. This is done using the "Tools/Add-Ins" option (Figure 2-15). Once the "Add-Ins" option is selected, a dialog box appears with several additional modules, one of which is the Data Analysis ToolPak. If we check the box next to "Analysis ToolPak" (Figure 2-16) and click on "OK," the ToolPak will be added and available under the "Tools" menu.

The Data Analysis ToolPak can be used to perform many statistical computations. Table 2-3 lists the analyses that are available through the Data Analysis ToolPak that we discussed in the textbook. Table 2-3 lists the procedures alphabetically along with the chapters from the textbook where procedures are discussed in more detail. (Excel does offer other procedures, but we restrict our attention to only those discussed in the textbook.)

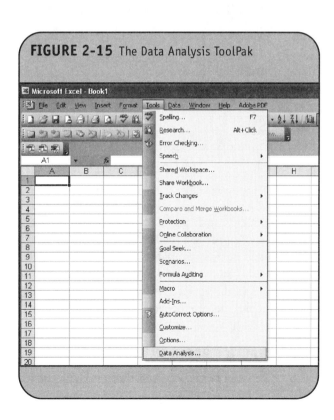

FIGURE 2-15 The Data Analysis ToolPak

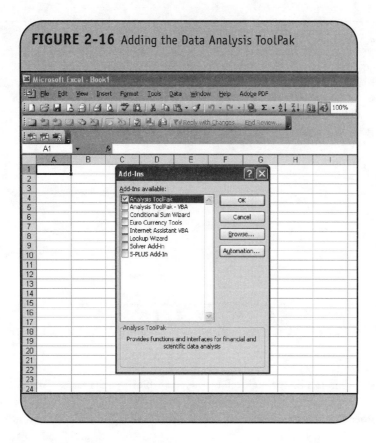

FIGURE 2-16 Adding the Data Analysis ToolPak

TABLE 2-3 Analysis Available in the Data Analysis ToolPak

Analysis	Chapter in Textbook
Analysis of variance	7
Descriptive statistics	4, 6
Histogram	4
Regression	8
t Test: Paired two sample for means	7
t Test: Two sample assuming equal variances	7
z Test: Two sample for means	7

There are some analyses (e.g., chi-square tests) that are not available in the Data Analysis ToolPak. In addition to the ToolPak, Excel also offers many statistical functions (e.g., CHITEST for a chi-square test) that can be used to perform specific tests and procedures. As we discuss specific analyses in Chapter 4 through Chapter 9 of the Excel workbook, we present options for analysis using the ToolPak and Excel's statistical functions.

2.5 PRACTICE PROBLEMS

1. Use Excel to create a worksheet, called *Data*, with the data in Table 2-4. The data were presented in Table 4-12 and were measured in a subsample of $n = 10$ participants who attended the seventh examination of the Framingham Offspring Study. Place the variable names in the first row of the worksheet.

2. Compute two new variables for each participant, body mass index (BMI) and mean arterial pressure (MAP). The formulas for the variables are:

$$BMI = \frac{weight_{pounds} \times 0.4536}{(height_{inches} \times 0.0254)^2}$$

$$MAP = \frac{(2 \times \text{Diastolic Blood Pressure}) + \text{Systolic Blood Pressure}}{3}$$

3. Compute the sample size for the MAP data using the COUNT function and store the result in the *Data* worksheet.

4. Compute the mean MAP by programming the formula for the mean (i.e., $\overline{X} = \frac{\Sigma X}{n}$) and store the result in the *Data* worksheet.

5. Compute the standard deviation of the MAP values by programming the formula for the standard deviation (i.e., $s = \sqrt{\frac{\Sigma(X - \overline{X})^2}{n - 1}}$) and store the result in the *Data* worksheet.

TABLE 2-4 Data for Practice Problems

Participant ID	Systolic Blood Pressure	Diastolic Blood Pressure	Total Serum Cholesterol	Weight (lb)	Height (in)
1	141	76	199	138	63.00
2	119	64	150	183	69.75
3	122	62	227	153	65.75
4	127	81	227	178	70.00
5	125	70	163	161	70.50
6	123	72	210	206	70.00
7	105	81	205	235	72.00
8	113	63	275	151	60.75
9	106	67	208	213	69.00
10	131	77	159	142	61.00

CHAPTER 3

Creating Tables and Graphs

Excel is very useful for creating tables and graphs to summarize and present statistical information. Many investigators use Excel to prepare tables and graphs for reports, presentations, and manuscripts. Often, presentations and manuscripts are prepared in other packages (e.g., PowerPoint, Word) but tables and charts are prepared in Excel and then imported into those presentations or manuscripts.

3.1 CREATING AND FORMATTING TABLES

In Chapter 4 of the textbook, we presented a number of statistics to summarize continuous, ordinal, and categorical variables. Investigators must determine which statistics most accurately and completely describe sample data. For example, for continuous variables we can compute the sample mean, median, and mode to describe central tendency and the sample range, interquartile range, variance, and standard deviation to describe variability. For ordinal and categorical variables, we can compute frequencies, relative frequencies, and cumulative relative frequencies (appropriate for ordinal variables). For presentation purposes, we must decide which statistics to present and how.

In almost all research reports, investigators include a description of the study sample. The description usually includes socio-demographic or background characteristics (e.g., age, gender, educational level) and might include data to describe clinical history (e.g., prevalent disease, symptom severity at the start of the study). With a cross-sectional or cohort study, the description is often based on the full sample or cohort. In clinical trials, descriptions are usually provided for each treatment group, considered separately. Regardless of whether data are presented for a single group or for separate groups, the investigator must select the most appropriate statistics to summarize key information.

Example 3.1. Suppose we conduct a cross-sectional study of 125 undergraduate students to estimate the prevalence of cigarette smoking. Before presenting data on the prevalence of smoking, the investigators wish to provide a description of the study sample. Suppose that several background variables are analyzed (with Excel or with another statistical computing package). For each continuous variable, sample means and standard deviations are produced, and for each ordinal and categorical variable, frequencies and relative frequencies are produced. The results are shown in Table 3-1.

Table 3-2 was developed in Excel to present the information shown here. For the continuous variables, we present means and standard deviations rounded to one decimal place. For ordinal and categorical variables, we present the frequencies and relative frequencies. The table can be copied from Excel into a Word document for presentation.

It is always important to include a clear and concise title in a table. It is also important to specify clear variable names with appropriate units. Finally, the data (i.e., summary statistics) presented in the table must be clearly defined. Table 3-2 was prepared in Excel, as shown in Figure 3-1.

The *title* is entered in the first row of the table. To accommodate the length of the title and lengths of variable names, the widths of the columns (e.g., A, B) in the worksheet can be increased. It is not necessary to enlarge all of column A to accommodate the long title because the title only occupies one row (the first row). To accommodate the length of the title, we merge cell A1 and cell B1 into one larger cell. This is done by

TABLE 3-1 Summary Statistics on Background Variables

Age	$\overline{X} = 19.567$		$s = 1.867$	
Sex	Men		Women	
	79 (63.2%)		46 (36.8%)	
Year in school	Freshmen	Sophomore	Junior	Senior
	35 (28.0%)	41 (32.8%)	31 (24.8%)	18 (14.4%)
Number of hours of exercise per week	$\overline{X} = 5.821$		$s = 2.989$	
Weight	$\overline{X} = 165.352$		$s = 14.857$	
Height	$\overline{X} = 67.463$		$s = 4.655$	

TABLE 3-2 Description of Study Sample

Characteristic	Mean (SD) or *n* (%)
Age (years)	19.6 (1.9)
Gender	
Men	79 (63%)
Women	46 (37%)
Year in School	
Freshmen	35 (28%)
Sophomore	41 (33%)
Junior	31 (25%)
Senior	18 (14%)
Exercise per week (h)	5.8 (3.0)
Weight (lb)	165.4 (14.9)
Height (in)	67.5 (4.7)

FIGURE 3-1 Description of Study Sample

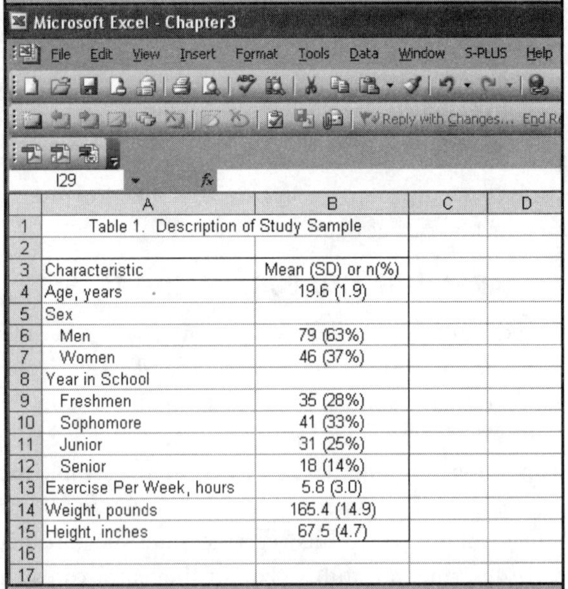

	A	B	C	D
1	Table 1. Description of Study Sample			
2				
3	Characteristic	Mean (SD) or n(%)		
4	Age, years	19.6 (1.9)		
5	Sex			
6	Men	79 (63%)		
7	Women	46 (37%)		
8	Year in School			
9	Freshmen	35 (28%)		
10	Sophomore	41 (33%)		
11	Junior	31 (25%)		
12	Senior	18 (14%)		
13	Exercise Per Week, hours	5.8 (3.0)		
14	Weight, pounds	165.4 (14.9)		
15	Height, inches	67.5 (4.7)		
16				
17				

first entering the title into cell A1. Because the title is longer than the width of the A1 cell, the title runs across into cell B1 through cell D1, as shown in Figure 3-2.

Before we merge cells to accommodate the length of the title, we first resize column A and column B to accommodate the variable names, units, and the descriptive statistics. To increase the width of column A, we place the cursor on the vertical line between column A and column B. The cursor changes shape to a bold cross with arrows running right and left. Moving the cursor on the vertical line between column A and column B to the right or to the left increases or decreases the width of column A. We do the same for column B with the vertical line between column B and column C. Figure 3-3 shows the widened column A and column B.

We now merge cell A1 and cell B1 to accommodate the width of the title. This is done by highlighting cell A1 and cell B1 and clicking on the "Merge and Center" icon shown on the menu bar (see Figure 3-3). The result is shown in Figure 3-4. We now enter the variable names, units, and the summary statistics into column A and column B.

Excel can be used to create tables for presentation purposes and it offers options similar to those offered in Word for formatting text in terms of font size, type, justification, and so on. Excel also has options to round numeric information—for example, to round statistics to one or two decimal places.

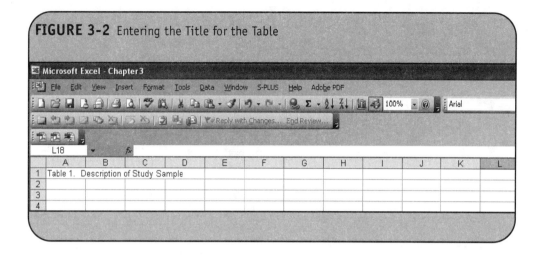

FIGURE 3-2 Entering the Title for the Table

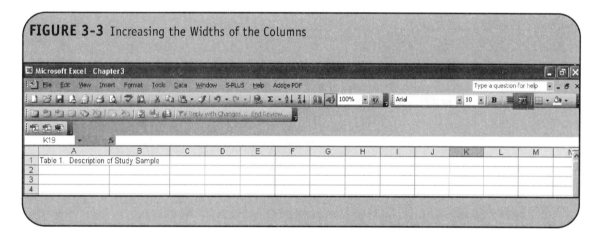

FIGURE 3-3 Increasing the Widths of the Columns

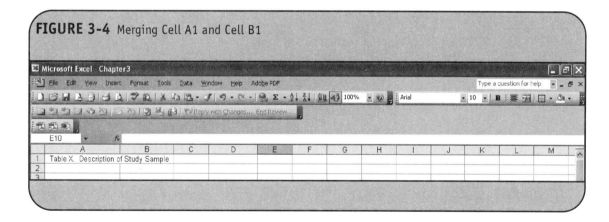

FIGURE 3-4 Merging Cell A1 and Cell B1

Suppose we compute the mean and standard deviation of several continuous variables as shown in Figure 3-5. For presentation, we wish to display the summary statistics to one decimal place. This can be done by first highlighting the desired range of cells (B2 through C5), and then selecting the "Format/Cells" option (Figure 3-6).

Once the "Format/Cells" menu option is selected, a dialog box appears. Various options are available for formatting. To format the numerical values to one decimal place, we select the "Number" category and then the desired number of decimal places. Here we choose one decimal place, as shown in Figure 3-7. Once we click "OK," the data are formatted to one decimal place.

FIGURE 3-5 Summary Statistics for Continuous Variables

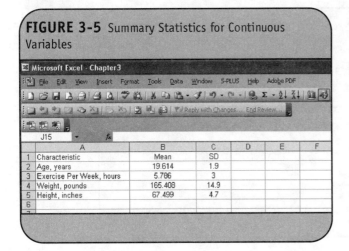

FIGURE 3-6 Formatting Statistics

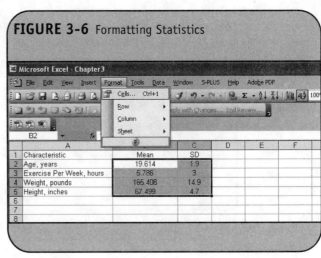

FIGURE 3-7 Formatting Numeric Data

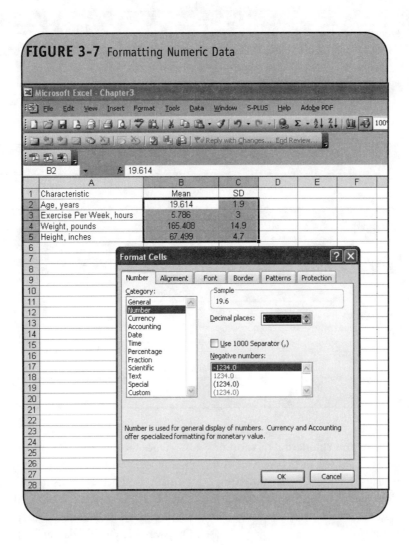

3.2   FREQUENCY DISTRIBUTION TABLES

Excel has a built-in menu option that can be used to create frequency tables for presenting information. This is especially useful for ordinal and categorical variables. The option is illustrated below.

Example 3.2. Suppose we have a small study of $n = 10$ patients with rheumatoid arthritis and we record their gender and the severity of their symptoms of arthritis. The data are shown in Figure 3-8. Suppose we want to present the gender distribution of the sample in a frequency distribution table. We first select the "Data" option on the main menu bar and then the "Pivot Table and Pivot Chart Report" option, as shown in Figure 3-9. Once we select this option, Excel opens the "Pivot Table and Pivot Chart Wizard," as shown in Figure 3-10.

The wizard essentially asks for the details necessary to generate the frequency distribution table. The first detail concerns the data. Excel asks where the data reside and the default response is a Microsoft Office Excel list or database, and this response is already checked. This response applies when the data are in an Excel worksheet, as is the case here. Thus, we do not need to modify the default response. We would choose an alternate response if, for example, the data were stored in a different file. The second detail concerns the type of report we wish to produce. The default response is checked and is a pivot table. This again is the appropriate response for a frequency distribution table. Once we click "Next," we are presented with a second dialog box, as shown in Figure 3-11.

Excel then asks specifically for the range of cells containing the study data. We want to generate a frequency distribution table for gender, so we specify cell B1 through cell B11. Notice that we include cell B1, which actually contains the name of the variable as opposed to data (Figure 3-12).

Once we click "Next," we are presented with a third dialog box where Excel asks for the location for the resultant frequency distribution table (see Figure 3-13). We need only to specify the cell address for the top-left corner of the frequency distribution table. We request that Excel places the top-left corner of the frequency distribution table in cell E1. (Note that we could have checked the first option and requested that the frequency distribution table be placed in a different worksheet.) When we click "Finish," Excel sets up a template in the current worksheet for the frequency distribution table. The template is shown in Figure 3-14. Notice that the top-left corner of the template is in cell E1.

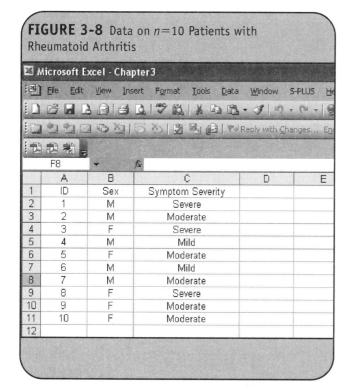

FIGURE 3-8 Data on $n=10$ Patients with Rheumatoid Arthritis

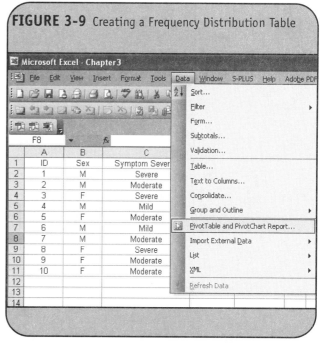

FIGURE 3-9 Creating a Frequency Distribution Table

FIGURE 3-10 Creating a Frequency Distribution Table

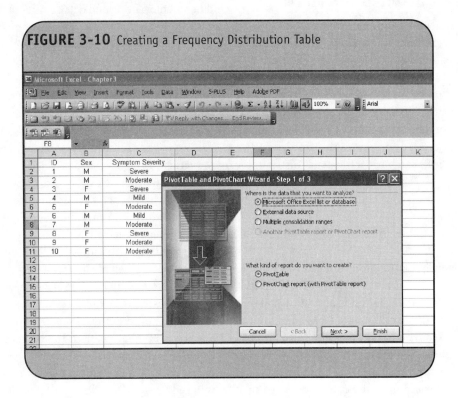

FIGURE 3-11 Creating a Frequency Distribution Table

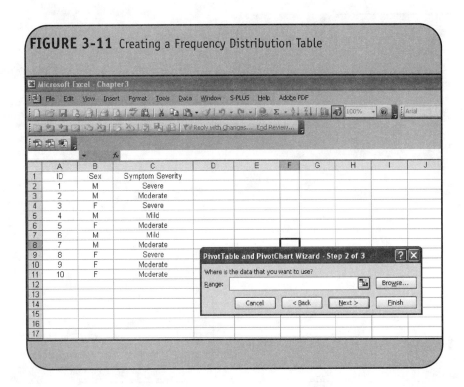

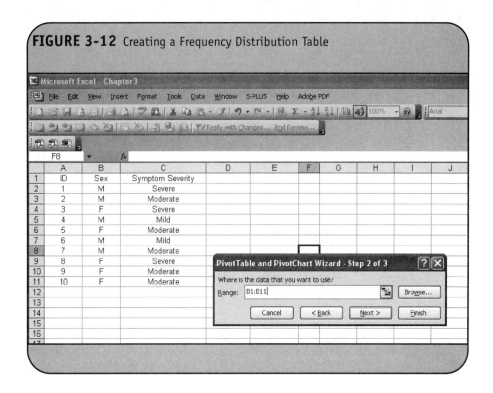

FIGURE 3-12 Creating a Frequency Distribution Table

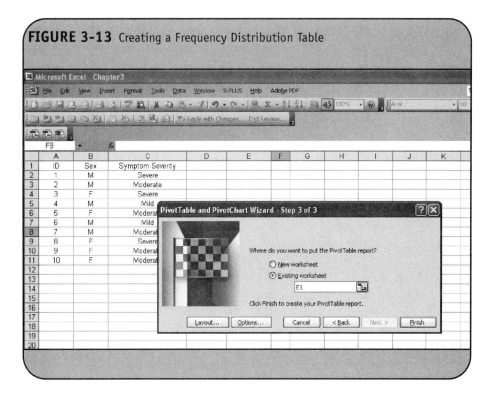

FIGURE 3-13 Creating a Frequency Distribution Table

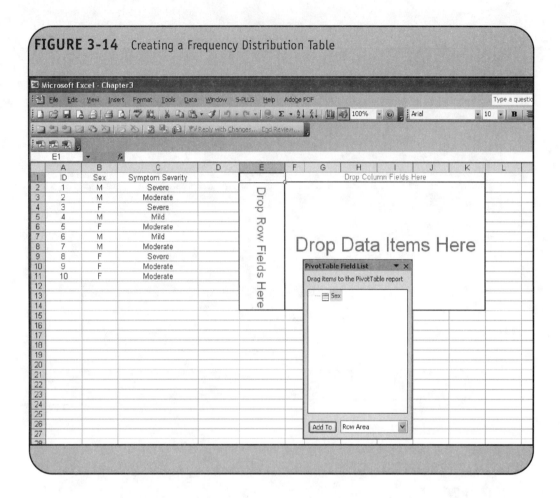

FIGURE 3-14   Creating a Frequency Distribution Table

In addition to the template (shown in the background), Excel also displays the variable we specified for the analysis (in this case, *Sex*) in the pivot table field list. To produce the frequency distribution table, we must specify that *Sex* is the row variable for the table and, in addition, that *Sex* is the data variable. We first specify that *Sex* is the row variable by clicking the "Add To" button in the dialog box. The variable *Sex* is specified in the list and we are requesting that Excel use *Sex* in the row area. Once we click "Add To," Excel automatically makes *Sex* the row variable in the frequency distribution table, as shown in Figure 3-15.

We now need to specify that *Sex* is also the data variable. The data variable is the variable that will be summarized. For a frequency distribution table on one variable, the row and data variable are the same. In other instances, it may be of interest to summarize a second variable (e.g., compute frequencies of symptom severity by gender, in which

case the data variable would be different from the row variable). This is done by selecting "Data Area" from the drop-down list at the bottom of the dialog box and clicking "Add To." This is shown in Figure 3-16. Once we add *Gender* to the data area, the frequency distribution table is generated by Excel (Figure 3-17).

Using the same sequence of steps, we can also generate a frequency distribution table for symptom severity. The results are shown in Figure 3-18. In the specifications, we requested that Excel place the top-left corner of the frequency distribution table in cell E7.

Suppose we also wanted to present relative frequencies. The relative frequencies for men and women can be computed by entering "=F3/$F$5" and "=F4/$F$5" into cell G3 and cell G4, respectively. The same can be done for the symptom severity data using "=F9/$F$12" in cell G9 and copying to cell G10 and cell G11. The results are shown in Figure 3-19.

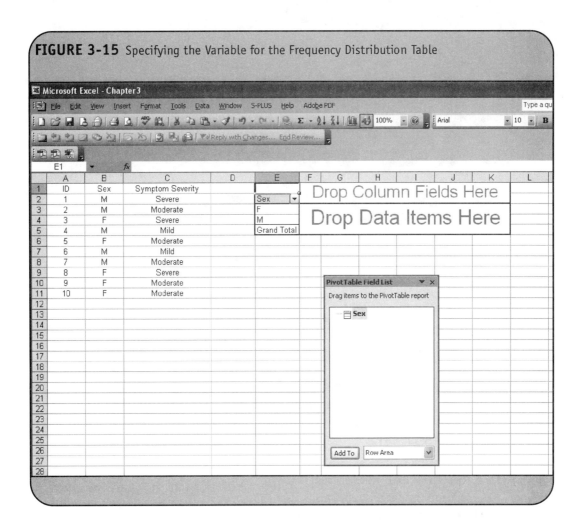

FIGURE 3-15 Specifying the Variable for the Frequency Distribution Table

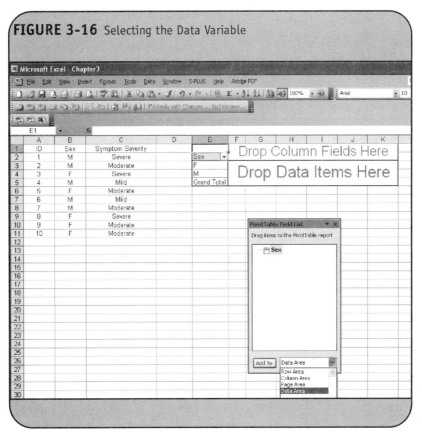

FIGURE 3-16 Selecting the Data Variable

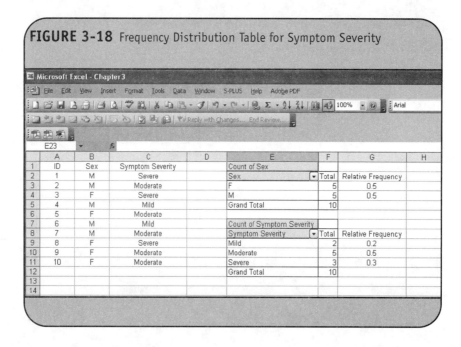

FIGURE 3-17 Frequency Distribution Table for Gender

	A	B	C	D	E	F	G	H
1	ID	Sex	Symptom Severity		Count of Sex			
2	1	M	Severe		Sex	Total		
3	2	M	Moderate		F	5		
4	3	F	Severe		M	5		
5	4	M	Mild		Grand Total	10		
6	5	F	Moderate					
7	6	M	Mild					
8	7	M	Moderate					
9	8	F	Severe					
10	9	F	Moderate					
11	10	F	Moderate					
12								
13								

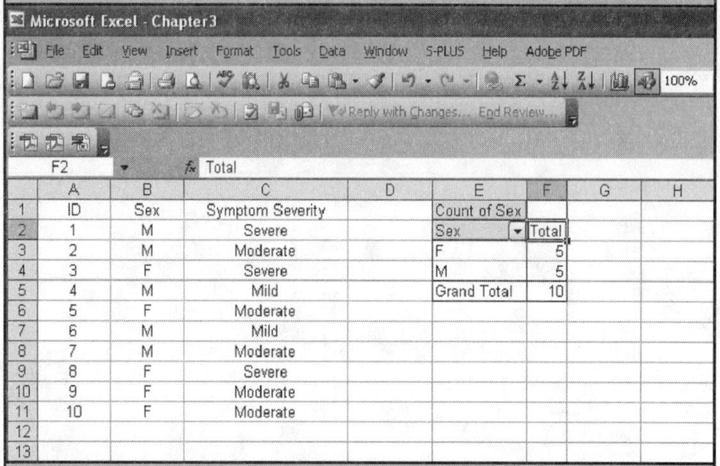

3.3 HISTOGRAMS AND BAR CHARTS

Excel is very powerful for generating graphical displays. Investigators often run statistical analyses in other packages such as SAS and then use Excel to produce graphical displays of the statistical results. There are several ways to generate histograms and bar charts for ordinal and categorical variables, respectively. We describe two techniques. The first is a follow-on to the "Data/Pivot Table and Pivot Chart Report" menu option, and the second uses the Excel Chart Wizard.

Similar to the wizard we used to create frequency distribution tables in the preceding section, Excel has a Chart Wizard that is very useful for generating graphical displays. The Chart Wizard can be accessed through the graphic icon on the main toolbar, as shown in Figure 3-20.

Clicking on the Chart Wizard opens the dialog box shown in Figure 3-20, which offers various options for graphical displays. Excel offers a number of standard graphical displays as well as some custom displays (under the respective tabs). We first illustrate how to produce a graphical display following the

FIGURE 3-18 Frequency Distribution Table for Symptom Severity

	A	B	C	D	E	F	G	H
1	ID	Sex	Symptom Severity		Count of Sex			
2	1	M	Severe		Sex	Total	Relative Frequency	
3	2	M	Moderate		F	5	0.5	
4	3	F	Severe		M	5	0.5	
5	4	M	Mild		Grand Total	10		
6	5	F	Moderate					
7	6	M	Mild		Count of Symptom Severity			
8	7	M	Moderate		Symptom Severity	Total	Relative Frequency	
9	8	F	Severe		Mild	2	0.2	
10	9	F	Moderate		Moderate	5	0.5	
11	10	F	Moderate		Severe	3	0.3	
12					Grand Total	10		
13								
14								

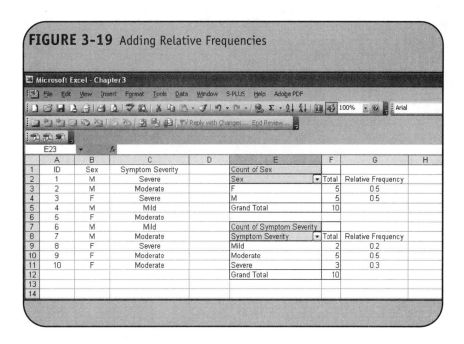

FIGURE 3-19 Adding Relative Frequencies

"Data/Pivot Table and Pivot Chart Report" option, and then using the Chart Wizard.

In Example 3.1 of the Excel workbook, we used the "Data/Pivot Table and Pivot Chart Report" to generate frequency distribution tables for gender and symptom severity. Once a frequency distribution table is produced, we can easily generate a graphical display. Suppose we want to generate a histogram for the distribution of symptom severity. This is done by selecting (highlighting) the frequency distribution for symptom severity and then clicking on the Chart Wizard (Figure 3-21). Once we click on the Chart Wizard, a new worksheet is generated, as shown in Figure 3-22. The new worksheet is called *Chart 1.* (This is the default name, but it can be changed.)

There are a number of options available for formatting the display. First, we can hide some of the templates and labels that Excel has placed on the display. This can be done by plac-

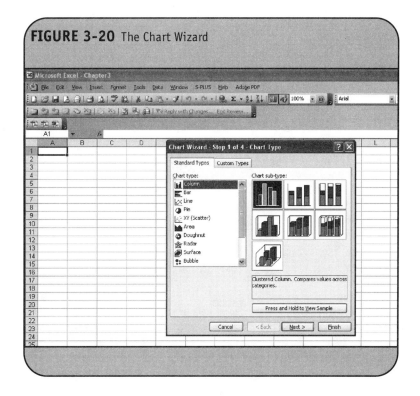

FIGURE 3-20 The Chart Wizard

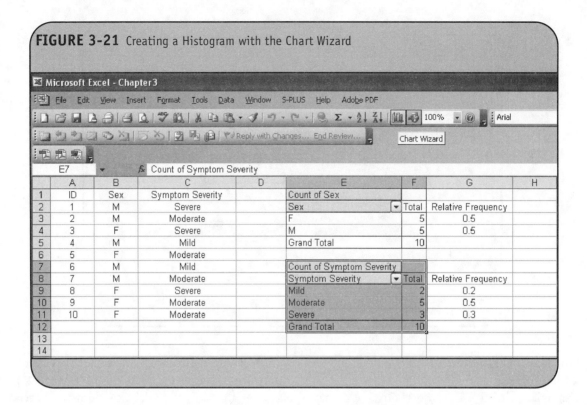

FIGURE 3-21 Creating a Histogram with the Chart Wizard

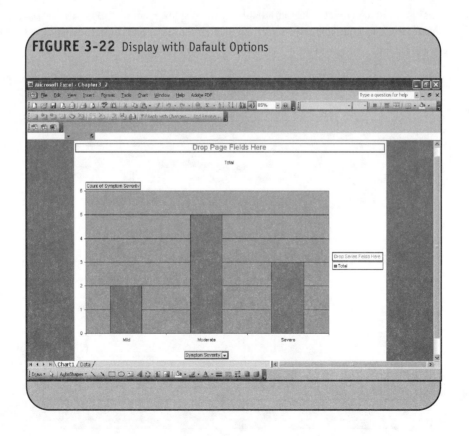

FIGURE 3-22 Display with Dafault Options

ing the cursor over the label, "Count of Symptom Severity." If we right-click while over this label, several options are available (Figure 3-23). When we click on "Hide Pivot Chart Field Buttons," the field labels are removed, producing the display shown in Figure 3-24.

Notice in Figure 3-24 that we also changed the title. This is done by double-clicking on the default title ("Total") and when the default title is highlighted, we enter a new title ("Frequency Histogram of Symptom Severity"). By default, Excel generates a bar chart. Because symptom severity is an

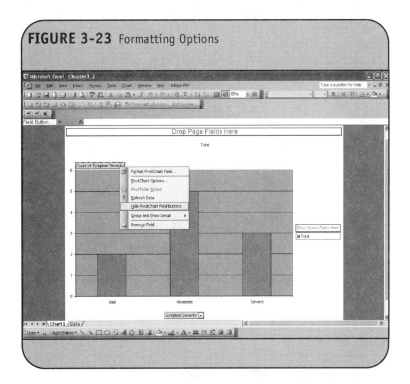

FIGURE 3-23 Formatting Options

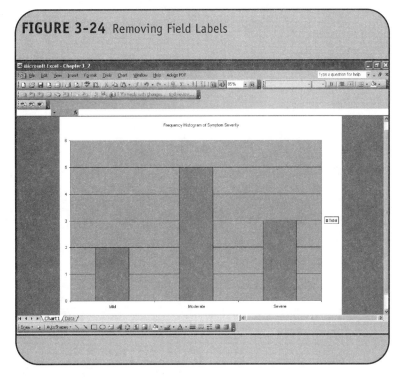

FIGURE 3-24 Removing Field Labels

ordinal variable and not a categorical variable, we want to display a histogram (i.e., the adjacent bars should run together). To change the bar chart into a histogram, we double-click on one of the three bars (double-clicking on any of the three will produce the same result). Double-clicking opens the menu of formatting options shown in Figure 3-25.

To convert the bar chart to a histogram, we select the "Options" tab, shown in Figure 3-26. The default gap width between bars is 150. To produce a histogram, we change the gap width to 0 (Figure 3-27). Once we click "OK," Excel generates the histogram shown in Figure 3-28.

Excel offers many options for formatting graphical displays. We described only a few here. A second method for generating graphical displays uses the Chart Wizard directly (i.e., does not involve first using the "Data/Pivot Table and Pivot Chart Report").

Example 3.3. In Example 4.2 in the textbook, we presented data from the seventh examination of the Offspring in the Framingham Heart Study ($n = 3539$) on blood pressure. Systolic and diastolic blood pressures were measured as continuous variables and organized into ordinal categories. Table 4-5 in the textbook showed a frequency distribution table for the ordinal blood pressure variable and is copied here in Table 3-3.

We want to generate a relative frequency histogram to present the blood pressure data. We first enter the information shown in Table 3-3 into Excel. Figure 3-29 contains the

TABLE 3-3 Frequency Distribution Table for Blood Pressure Categories

Blood Pressure	Frequency	Relative Frequency (%)
Normal	1206	34.1
Pre-hypertension	1452	41.1
Stage I hypertension	653	18.5
Stage II hypertension	222	6.3
Total	3533	100.0

FIGURE 3-25 Formatting the Bars

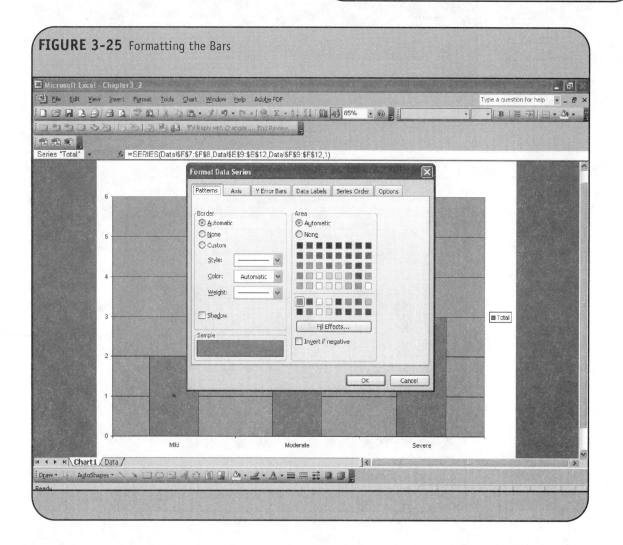

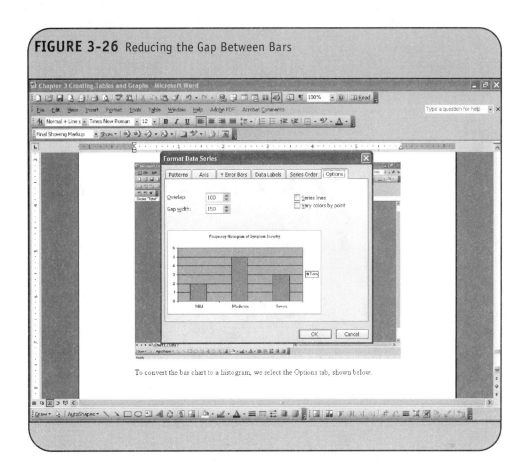

FIGURE 3-26 Reducing the Gap Between Bars

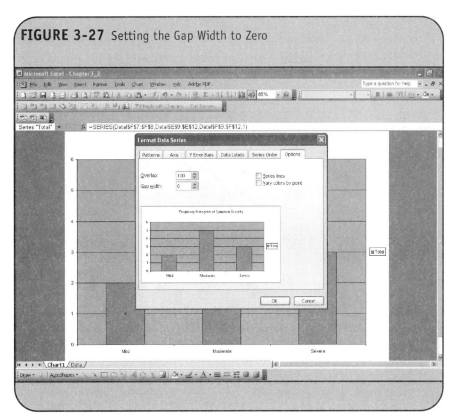

FIGURE 3-27 Setting the Gap Width to Zero

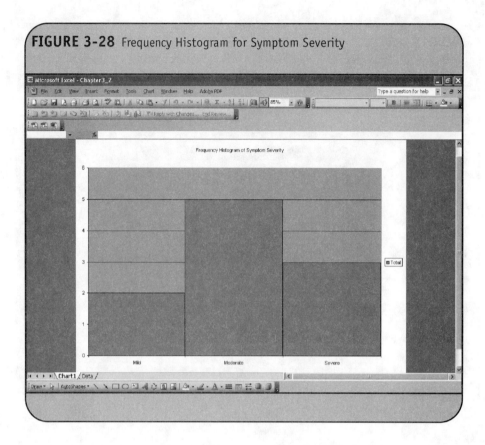

FIGURE 3-28 Frequency Histogram for Symptom Severity

data. To generate the relative frequency histogram, we click the Chart Wizard icon on the menu bar. This opens the dialog box shown in Figure 3-30 with various options.

The first option is a column chart, and Excel will generate various forms of this display (e.g., one-dimensional, three-dimensional). Suppose we click the top-left option (the default

option shown in black in Figure 3-30) under "Chart Subtype." Once we click "Next," Excel then asks for the range of the data for the display (Figure 3-31).

We specify both the location of the response labels (to label the bars) and the location of the relative frequencies. The responses are in column A and the relative frequencies are in

FIGURE 3-29 Blood Pressure Data

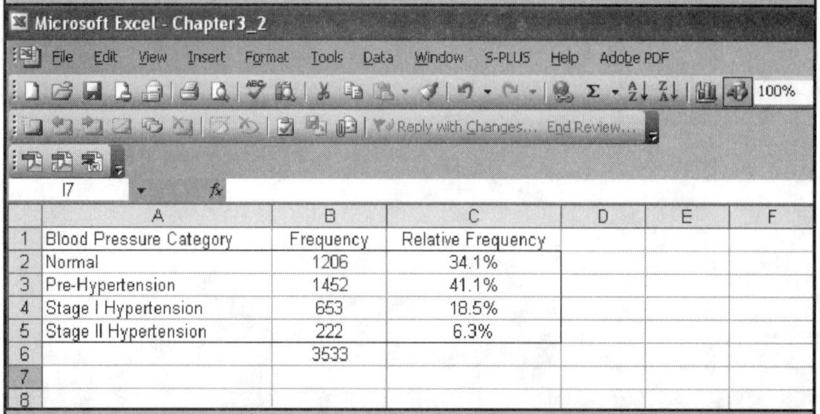

	A	B	C	D	E	F
1	Blood Pressure Category	Frequency	Relative Frequency			
2	Normal	1206	34.1%			
3	Pre-Hypertension	1452	41.1%			
4	Stage I Hypertension	653	18.5%			
5	Stage II Hypertension	222	6.3%			
6		3533				
7						
8						

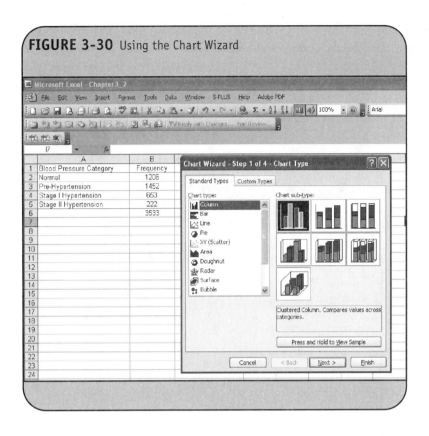

FIGURE 3-30 Using the Chart Wizard

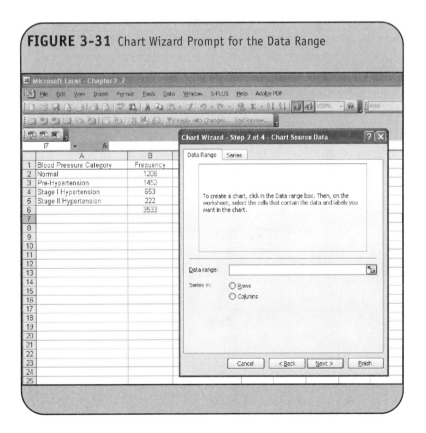

FIGURE 3-31 Chart Wizard Prompt for the Data Range

column C. The data are specified as "A1:A5,C1:C5." The first range contains the response labels and the second range contains the relative frequencies (Figure 3-32).

When we click "Next," Excel provides a snapshot of the display and opens a dialog box with a number of formatting options (Figure 3-33). The first tab contains options for labels and titles. The chart title is entered first, followed by labels for the *x*- and *y*-axis of the display (Figure 3-34). At this stage, we can also format other aspects of the display by selecting other tabs that are shown in Figure 3-34. However, if we click "Next," Excel asks for the location of the display (Figure 3-35).

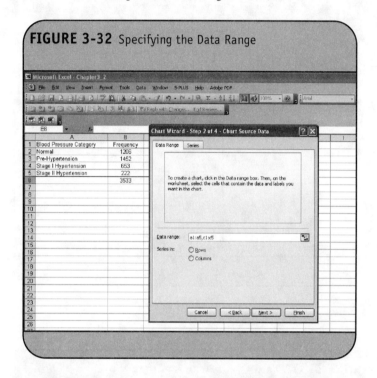

FIGURE 3-32 Specifying the Data Range

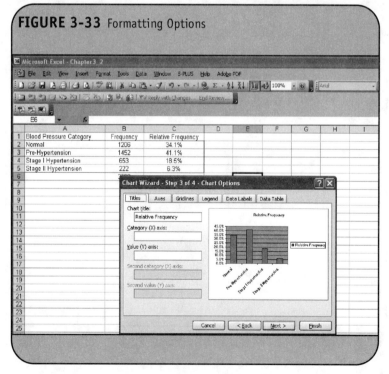

FIGURE 3-33 Formatting Options

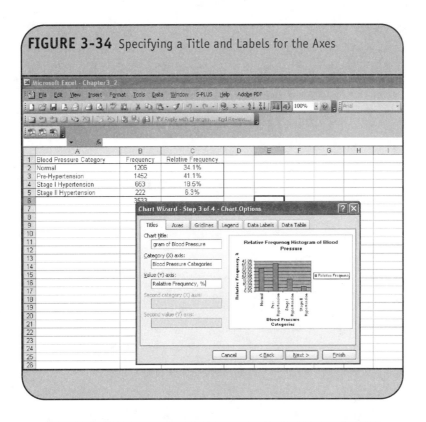

FIGURE 3-34 Specifying a Title and Labels for the Axes

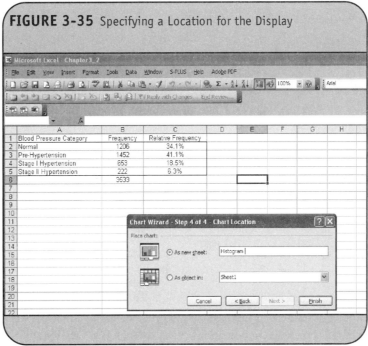

FIGURE 3-35 Specifying a Location for the Display

We can place the display in a new worksheet—in which case, we provide a name for the new worksheet—or we can place the display in the current worksheet. In Figure 3-35, we specify that we would like the display placed in a new worksheet called *Histogram*. We click "Finish" and

Excel generates the new worksheet containing the display (Figure 3-36).

We can continue to format the display. We first reduce the gap width between adjacent bars to zero by double-clicking on any of the bars, which opens the dialog box shown

FIGURE 3-36 The Display

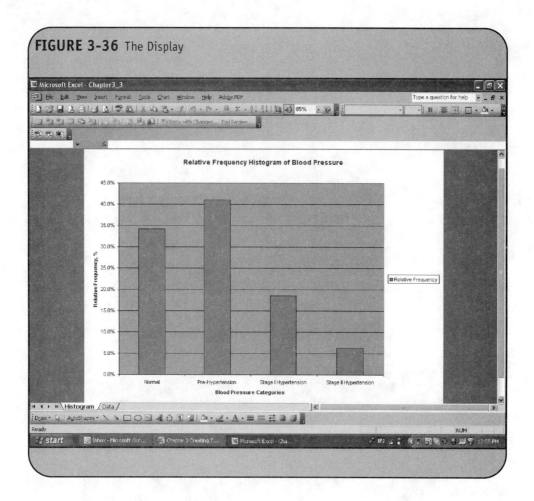

in Figure 3-27, and we specify a gap width of 0. We then remove the label on the right side ("Relative Frequency") by right-clicking on the label and clicking "Clear." We then remove the grey background by double-clicking anywhere in the background. This opens a dialog box where we can either select another color or choose "None" under the "Area" section for no background color. Finally, we remove the horizontal lines by right-clicking on any line and clicking "Delete." (Excel also has a "Clear" option, which can be used to remove the horizontal lines.) After implementing these steps, the histogram is as shown in Figure 3-37.

3.4 SCATTER DIAGRAMS

A popular graphical display to illustrate the relationship between two continuous variables is a scatter diagram. Scatter diagrams are useful in linear regression analysis applications (see Chapter 9 of the textbook) to assess the relationship between a continuous independent and a continuous dependent variable.

Example 3.4. Suppose we wish to examine the association between body mass index (BMI) and systolic blood pressure (SBP) in a sample of $n = 12$ persons who are not taking antihypertensive medication. The data are entered into an Excel worksheet as shown in Figure 3-38.

To generate the scatter diagram, we again use the Chart Wizard. However, rather than specifying the data for the display in the dialog box that appears as part of the Chart Wizard (Figure 3-32), we illustrate an alternative approach. Here we first highlight the data for the display (in this case, cell B1 through cell C13) and then click on the Chart Wizard icon. From the list of "Standard Chart Types," we select "XY (Scatter)" as shown in Figure 3-39.

Recall that in regression analysis, we use x to denote the independent variable and y to denote the dependent variable (see Chapter 9 of the textbook). In this example, BMI is the independent variable and SBP is the dependent variable. Excel assumes that the first variable specified is the independent (x) and the second is the dependent (y). This is the way the data in Example 3.4 are organized. The default subtype (shown in black in Figure 3-39) is the scatter diagram. The other subtypes connect the data either with lines or curves, depending on which subtype is selected. Once we

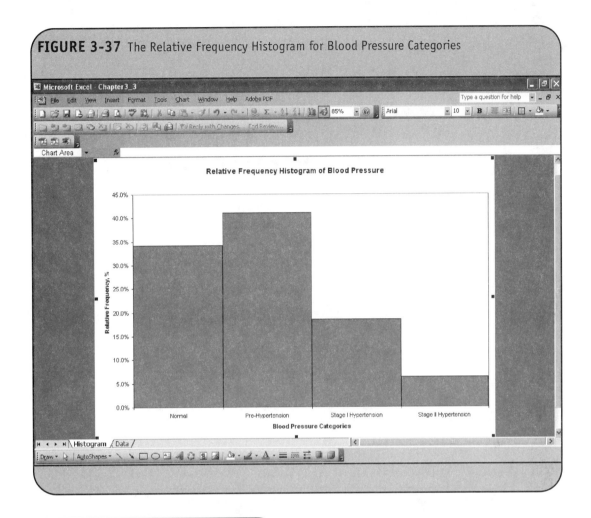

FIGURE 3-37 The Relative Frequency Histogram for Blood Pressure Categories

FIGURE 3-38 Data for Scatter Diagram

	A	B	C	D	E	F
1	ID	BMI	SBP			
2	1	24.3	120			
3	2	28.5	140			
4	3	32.1	135			
5	4	22.9	115			
6	5	23.5	127			
7	6	40.2	165			
8	7	38.4	142			
9	8	37.5	139			
10	9	33.2	145			
11	10	34.1	136			
12	11	26.3	138			
13	12	24.5	125			
14						
15						

click "Next," Excel displays a template of the scatter diagram along with a dialog box in which the range of the data are indicated (Figure 3-40). Note that the data range is automatically filled (we actually selected the data range before invoking the Chart Wizard).

We click "Next" and are presented with a template of the scatter diagram and options for formatting (Figure 3-41). We can input a title as well as labels for the *x* (horizontal) and *y* (vertical) axes. We can use the other options to remove the gridlines and the legend. When we click "Next," Excel asks for a location for the scatter diagram (Figure 3-42).

We can place the scatter diagram in a new worksheet—in which case, we provide a name for the new worksheet—or we can place the display in the current worksheet. In Figure 3-42, we specify that we would like the display placed in a new worksheet called *Scatter Diagram*. We click "Finish" and Excel generates the new worksheet containing the display (Figure 3-43).

Excel automatically scales the *x*- and *y*-axes from zero to a value larger than the maximum value in the dataset. There

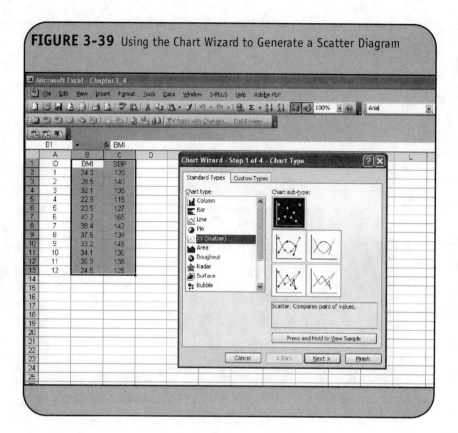

FIGURE 3-39 Using the Chart Wizard to Generate a Scatter Diagram

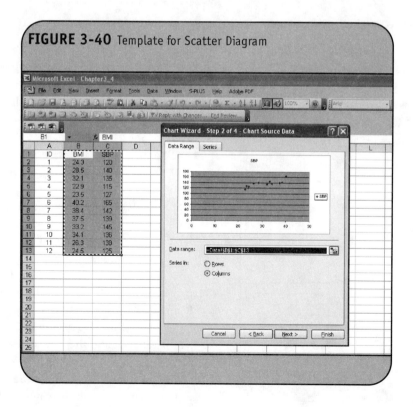

FIGURE 3-40 Template for Scatter Diagram

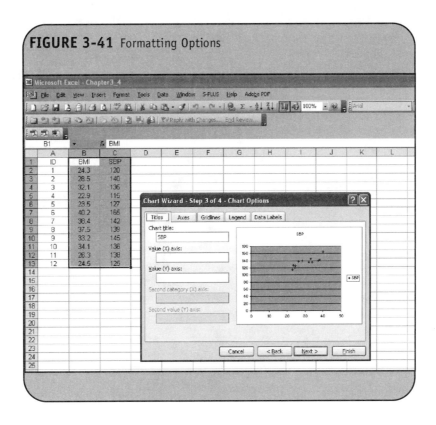

FIGURE 3-41 Formatting Options

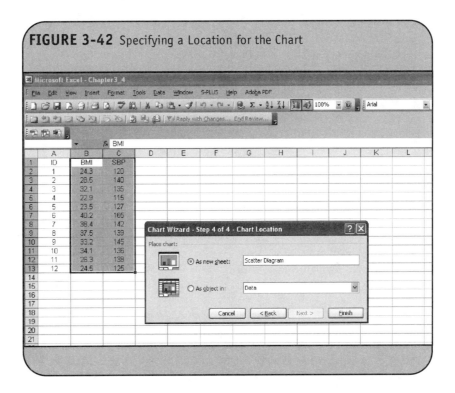

FIGURE 3-42 Specifying a Location for the Chart

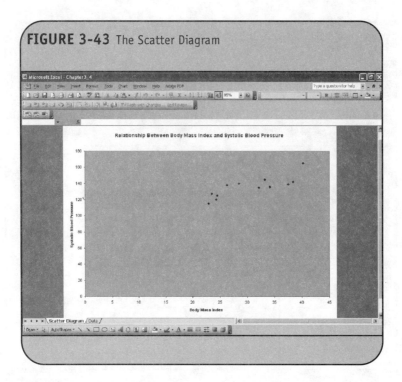

FIGURE 3-43 The Scatter Diagram

are many variables whose theoretical minimum is much larger than zero; BMI and SBP are two examples. Thus, we will next rescale the *x*- and *y*-axes to start at more reasonable values. For example, we will rescale the *x*-axis from 20 to 45 and the *y*-axis from 100 to 180. We first rescale the *x*-axis (BMI). This is done by double-clicking anywhere along the *x* axis. This brings up the dialog box shown in Figure 3-44.

In the dialog box, we choose the "Scale" tab and specify the desired minimum, maximum, and major unit. The major unit represents the distance between tick marks shown on that axis.

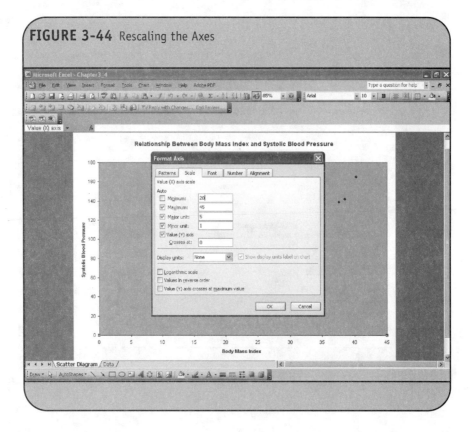

FIGURE 3-44 Rescaling the Axes

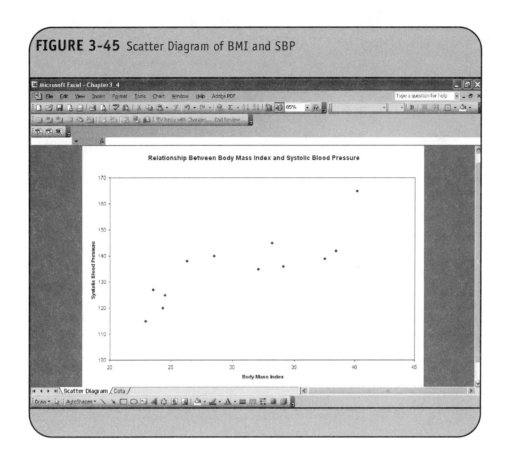

FIGURE 3-45 Scatter Diagram of BMI and SBP

When the data are entered, we click "OK." After following the same sequence for the *y*-axis (SBP) and changing the background from grey to white (i.e., double-clicking anywhere in the background, which opens a dialog box where we can either select another color or choose "None" under the "Area" section for no background color), the scatter diagram is as shown in Figure 3-45. We also remove the horizontal lines by right-clicking on any line and choosing "Delete" (or "Clear").

The scatter diagram illustrates the positive association between body mass index and systolic blood pressure. The scatter diagram can now be copied from Excel into a manuscript, report, or presentation.

3.5   PRACTICE PROBLEMS

1.   The data in Table 3-4 were measured in $n = 15$ college seniors in a cross-sectional study of alcohol consumption. Each participant was asked their gender, year in school, the age at which they first consumed alcohol, and the number of alcoholic drinks they consume on a typical drinking night. Generate frequency distribution tables for gender and

year in school using the "Data/Pivot Table and Pivot Chart Report" option on the menu bar.

2.   Generate a frequency bar chart for gender using the Pivot Table and Pivot Chart Report.

3.   Generate a frequency histogram for year in school using the Pivot Table and Pivot Chart.

4.   Create a frequency distribution table for drinking status, defined by the following numbers of drinks per night:

Abstinent	0
Light	1–3
Moderate	4–5
Heavy	6 or more

5.   Generate a frequency histogram for drinking status using the Chart Wizard.

6.   Generate a scatter diagram to display the association between age at first drink and number of drinks per night. (Note that the sample size for analysis is $n = 13$.)

TABLE 3-4 Data for Practice Problem

ID Number	Gender	Year in School	Age at First Drink*	Number of Drinks/Night
1	M	Freshman	14	5
2	M	Senior	11	8
3	F	Junior	17	3
4	M	Junior	13	9
5	F	Freshman		0
6	F	Sophomore	15	4
7	F	Freshman	15	0
8	F	Freshman		0
9	M	Senior	15	7
10	F	Junior	21	5
11	M	Junior	18	3
12	M	Senior	14	6
13	F	Junior	19	3
14	F	Sophomore	18	2
15	M	Junior	20	4

Summarizing Continuous Variables in a Sample

In Chapter 4 of the textbook, we presented summary statistics for dichotomous, ordinal, categorical, and continuous variables. We discussed both numerical and graphical summaries. Numerical summaries for continuous variables include the sample mean, standard deviation, median, and quartiles. Numerical summaries for ordinal and categorical data use frequency distribution tables, and these were discussed in detail in Chapter 3 of the Excel workbook. In Chapter 3 of the Excel workbook, we also presented several graphical displays for sample data. Numerical summaries for continuous variables measured in a sample will be discussed here.

The most appropriate numerical summaries for continuous variables depend on whether or not there are outliers. Regardless of whether there are outliers, the summary should always include the sample size, a measure of central tendency or a typical value (e.g., the mean or median), and a measure of variability (e.g., standard deviation or interquartile range). Here we will generate summaries that include numerous statistics; the investigator must choose those that are most appropriate to summarize a particular characteristic.

4.1 THE DESCRIPTIVE STATISTICS ANALYSIS TOOL

Here we generate summary statistics on a continuous variable using the Descriptive Statistics Analysis Tool available in the Excel Data Analysis ToolPak.

Example 4.1. In Example 4.3 in the textbook, we analyzed data from a subset of $n = 10$ participants attending the seventh examination of the Offspring in the Framingham Heart Study. The data values were presented in Table 4-12 of the text and are shown here in Table 4-1.

The means, standard deviations, and other statistics can be computed using the Descriptive Statistics Analysis Tool in the Data Analysis ToolPak. Figure 4-1 shows the data entered into an Excel worksheet. We will now use the Data Analysis ToolPak to generate descriptive statistics on each continuous variable. We will begin with body mass index (BMI).

When we select the "Tools/Data Analysis" option from the menu bar, a dialog box with the various analysis tools appears (Figure 4-2). From the list of analysis tools, we choose "Descriptive Statistics." We are then presented with a second dialog box. Figure 4-3 displays this dialog box, which requires input for the descriptive statistics.

In the dialog box, we must provide the location of the data values we wish to summarize. This is requested under "Input Range." In the "Input Range," we specify cell G1 through cell G11. The data actually reside in cell G2 through cell G11, with the variable name in cell G1. We must check the box to indicate that the variable name or label is in the first row. By doing so, Excel will print the variable name on the output. If we do not check the box to indicate that the variable label is in the first row, then we must specify the input range as "G2:G11". In the next section of the dialog box, we specify where we would like the results placed. The options are to place the output in the current worksheet, in a new worksheet (within the same workbook), or in a new workbook. If we select output range, we must

TABLE 4-1 Subsample of $n = 10$ Participants Attending the Seventh Examination of the Framingham Offspring Study

Participant ID	Systolic Blood Pressure	Diastolic Blood Pressure	Total Serum Cholesterol	Weight (lb)	Height (in)	BMI
1	141	76	199	138	63.00	24.4
2	119	64	150	183	69.75	26.4
3	122	62	227	153	65.75	24.9
4	127	81	227	178	70.00	25.5
5	125	70	163	161	70.50	22.8
6	123	72	210	206	70.00	29.6
7	105	81	205	235	72.00	31.9
8	113	63	275	151	60.75	28.8
9	106	67	208	213	69.00	31.5
10	131	77	159	142	61.00	26.8

FIGURE 4-1 Data for Analysis Entered into Excel

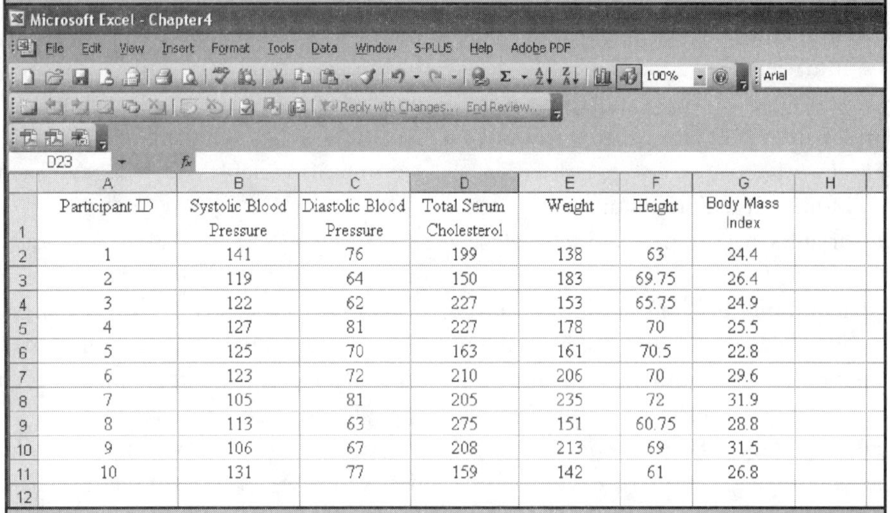

	A	B	C	D	E	F	G	H
1	Participant ID	Systolic Blood Pressure	Diastolic Blood Pressure	Total Serum Cholesterol	Weight	Height	Body Mass Index	
2	1	141	76	199	138	63	24.4	
3	2	119	64	150	183	69.75	26.4	
4	3	122	62	227	153	65.75	24.9	
5	4	127	81	227	178	70	25.5	
6	5	125	70	163	161	70.5	22.8	
7	6	123	72	210	206	70	29.6	
8	7	105	81	205	235	72	31.9	
9	8	113	63	275	151	60.75	28.8	
10	9	106	67	208	213	69	31.5	
11	10	131	77	159	142	61	26.8	
12								

specify the cell address for the top-left corner of the table containing the results (e.g., I1). In Figure 4-3, we select "New Worksheet Ply" (to place the results in a new worksheet in the same workbook) and we specify the name of the new worksheet as *Descriptive Statistics*. In the last section of the dialog box, we request that Excel generate summary statistics for BMI by checking the appropriate box in the dialog box. The results of the analysis are shown in Figure 4-4.

Notice that the results are contained in a new worksheet in the workbook, called *Descriptive Statistics*. The data are contained in the *Data* worksheet. By selecting the "Descriptive Statistics" option, Excel generates all of the statistics shown in Figure 4-4. In Chapter 4 of the textbook, we

FIGURE 4-2 Invoking the Data Analysis ToolPak

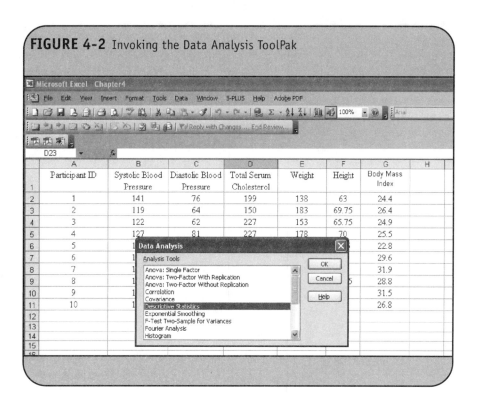

FIGURE 4-3 The Descriptive Statistics Analysis Tool

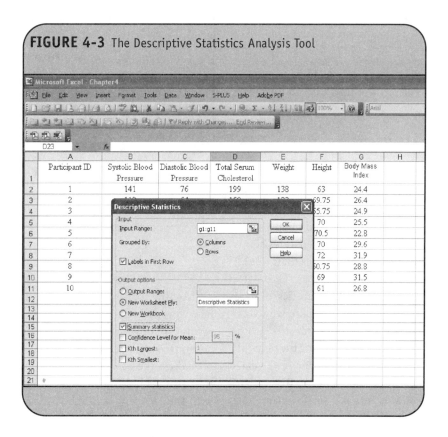

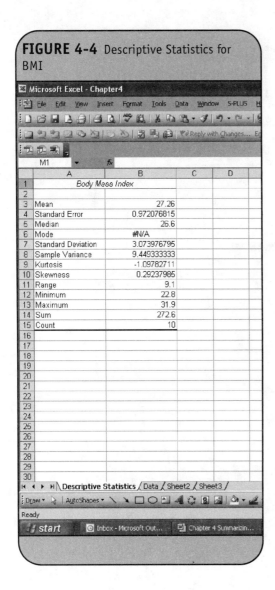

FIGURE 4-4 Descriptive Statistics for BMI

TABLE 4-2 Default Statistics in Descriptive Statistics Analysis Tool

Statistic	Formula/Description
Sample mean	$\overline{X} = \dfrac{\Sigma X}{n}$
Standard error	$SE = \dfrac{s}{\sqrt{n}}$
Median	Middle value (50% above and 50% below)
Mode	The most frequent value. If there is no value that appears more than any other, Excel indicates this with "#N/A"
Sample standard deviation	$s = \sqrt{\dfrac{\Sigma(X - \overline{X})^2}{n - 1}}$
Sample variance	$s^2 = \dfrac{\Sigma(X - \overline{X})^2}{n - 1}$
Kurtosis	Reflects the thickness of the tails of a distribution of a continuous characteristic as compared to a normal distribution (see Chapter 5 of the textbook). The kurtosis of a normal distribution is 0.
Skewness	Reflects the symmetry of a distribution of a continuous characteristic as compared to a normal distribution (see Chapter 5 of the textbook). The skewness of a normal distribution is 0.
Range	Range = Maximum − Minimum
Minimum	The smallest value in the dataset
Maximum	The largest value in the dataset
Sum	The sum of the observations, ΣX
Count	The number of observations, n

discussed many of these statistics (but not all). The most relevant statistics for BMI are the sample size (referred to as *Count*) $n = 10$, the sample mean $\overline{X} = 27.26$, and sample standard deviation $s = 3.07$. Notice that Excel generates summary statistics with many more decimal places than would be reasonable to report.

It is also possible to generate descriptive statistics for several continuous variables simultaneously. Again, we select "Tool/Data Analysis," and then "Descriptive Statistics" from the list of analysis tools. This is done by specifying the range of all variables in the input range in the first section of the dialog box. In Figure 4-5, we specify the input range as B1 through G11. This range includes all variables and variable names or labels (which are contained in row 1).

Again, we request that the output be placed in a new worksheet called *All Variables*. A screenshot of partial results is shown in Figure 4-6. Descriptive statistics are computed on each of the variables but cannot be displayed on the screen without substantially reducing the font size. The default (or automatic) statistics produced with the Descriptive Statistics Analysis Tool are shown in Table 4-2.

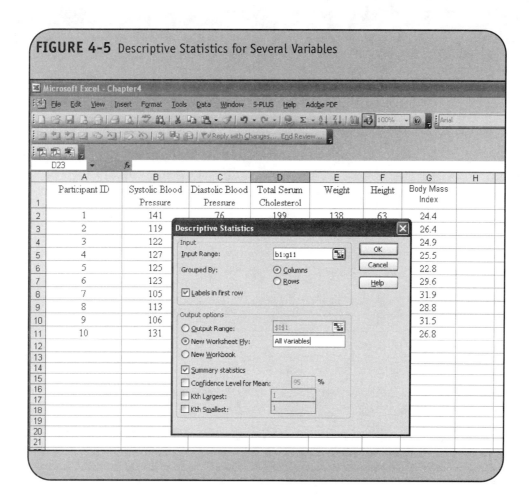

FIGURE 4-5 Descriptive Statistics for Several Variables

4.2 DESCRIPTIVE STATISTICS USING EXCEL FUNCTIONS

There are other statistics that we discussed in Chapter 4 of the textbook that are useful for continuous variables that are not automatically generated with the Descriptive Statistics Analysis Tool. An example is the first (and third) quartile. Excel does not include the quartiles in the output of the Descriptive Statistics Analysis Tool, but they can be computed with an Excel function. The function is "= QUARTILE(*data range, quartile number*)".

The data range is defined by the addresses of the cells containing the first and last observations in the dataset, separated by a colon. For example, using the data in Figure 4-1, systolic blood pressures occupy the range "B2:B11", diastolic blood pressures occupy the range "C2:C11," and total cholesterol values occupy the range "D2:D11". The quartile numbers range from 0 to 4. Table 4-3 indicates which values are generated for each quartile number.

We now use the quartile function to generate quartiles for the diastolic blood pressures (DBP) shown in Figure 4-1. In Figure 4-7, we use the quartile function to compute the first quartile of DBP and place it in cell C13. Notice that we also added a label into cell B13. In Figure 4-8, we compute the

TABLE 4-3 Quartiles Produced by the QUARTILE Function

Quartile Number	Statistic
0	Minimum
1	First quartile (holds 25% of values below it)
2	Median
3	Third quartile (holds 25% of values above it)
4	Maximum

FIGURE 4-6 Descriptive Statistics for All Variables

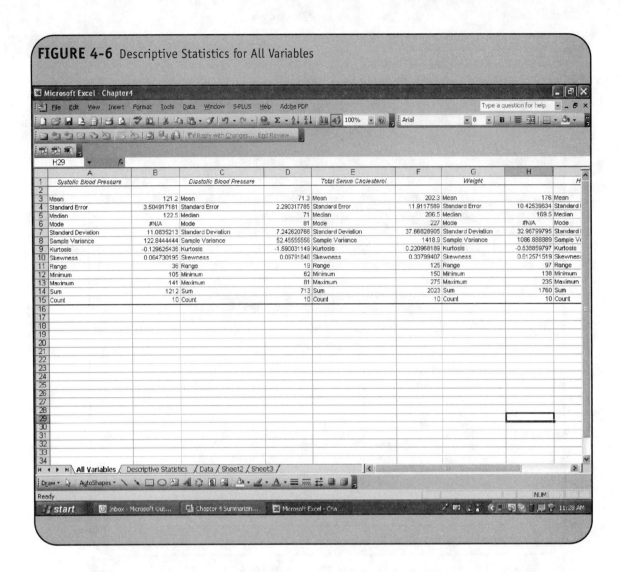

FIGURE 4-7 First Quartile of DBP

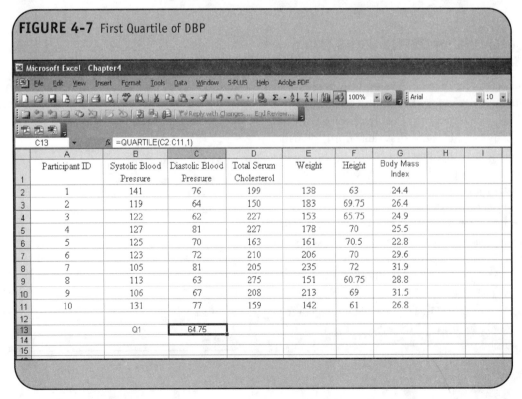

second (median) and third (Q3) quartiles of DBP. These are computed using the formulas "=QUARTILE(C2:C11,2)" and "=QUARTILE(C2:C11,3)", respectively.

Other Excel functions that are useful for generating summary statistics for continuous variables are shown in Table 4-4. For each function, the data (i.e., the range of cells in the worksheet containing the data to be analyzed) are specified in parentheses. The exception is the QUARTILE function, which also requires specification of the quartile number.

To compute the standard deviation of the systolic blood pressures, we enter "=STDEV(B2:B11)". Similarly, we can compute the median systolic blood pressure using the median function, "=MEDIAN(B2:B11)". Note that "=MEDIAN(B2:B11)" is equivalent to "=QUARTILE(B2:B11,2)". In Excel and in most other statistical computing packages, there are several ways to perform the same analysis. The analyst can choose the method with which they are the most comfortable or that best suits their style.

TABLE 4-4 Excel Functions for Summary Statistics

Function	Description
AVERAGE	Computes the sample mean
COUNT	Computes the sample size
MAX	Computes the maximum value
MEDIAN	Computes the sample median
MIN	Computes the minimum value
MODE	Computes the mode
QUARTILE	Computes the quartiles
STDEV	Computes the sample standard deviation
VAR	Computes the sample variance

FIGURE 4-8 Second and Third Quartiles of DBP

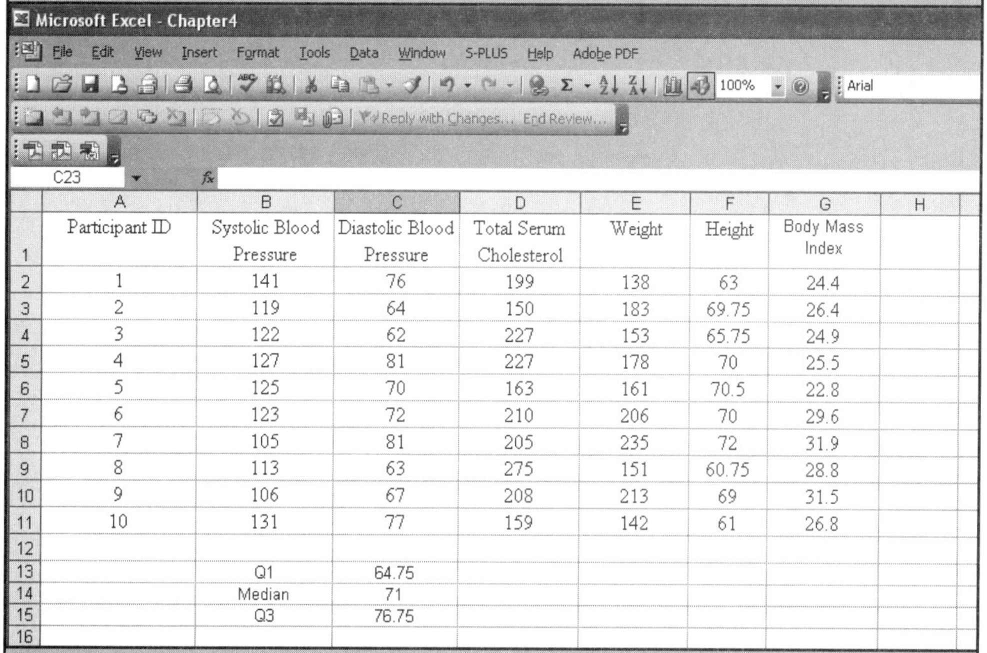

	A	B	C	D	E	F	G	H
1	Participant ID	Systolic Blood Pressure	Diastolic Blood Pressure	Total Serum Cholesterol	Weight	Height	Body Mass Index	
2	1	141	76	199	138	63	24.4	
3	2	119	64	150	183	69.75	26.4	
4	3	122	62	227	153	65.75	24.9	
5	4	127	81	227	178	70	25.5	
6	5	125	70	163	161	70.5	22.8	
7	6	123	72	210	206	70	29.6	
8	7	105	81	205	235	72	31.9	
9	8	113	63	275	151	60.75	28.8	
10	9	106	67	208	213	69	31.5	
11	10	131	77	159	142	61	26.8	
12								
13		Q1	64.75					
14		Median	71					
15		Q3	76.75					
16								

4.3   PRACTICE PROBLEMS

1. A study is conducted to estimate the mean total cholesterol level in children 2 to 6 years of age. A sample of nine participants is selected and their total cholesterol levels are measured as follows.

   185 225 240 196 175 180 194 147 223

   a. Use the Data Analysis ToolPak to compute the sample mean, standard deviation, and median.
   b. Use the QUARTILE function to compute the first and third quartiles.

2. The following data were collected as part of a study of coffee consumption among graduate students. The following reflects cups per day consumed:

   3   4   6   8   2   1   0   2

   a. Use the Data Analysis ToolPak to compute the sample mean, standard deviation, and median.
   b. Use the QUARTILE function to compute the first and third quartiles.

3. In the study of a new antihypertensive medication, systolic blood pressures are measured at baseline (or the start of the study before any treatment is administered). The data are as follows:

   120   112   138   145   135   150   145   163

   148   128   143   156   160   142   150

   Use Excel functions to compute the sample mean, standard deviation, median, and quartiles.

4. The following are height measurements (in cm) for a sample of infants participating in a study of infant health:

   28   30   41   48   29   48   62   49   51   39

   Use the Data Analysis ToolPak to compute summary statistics.

CHAPTER 5

Working with Probability Functions

Excel has a number of probability functions that can be used to compute probabilities or to find percentiles. In Chapter 5 of the textbook, we discussed in detail two probability models, the binomial and normal distributions, which are appropriate for dichotomous and continuous outcomes, respectively. As we discussed in Chapter 5 of the textbook, there are many other probability distributions that describe discrete and continuous outcomes; we focused exclusively on these two. Excel has a number of probability functions that can be used to compute probabilities for various distributions. We will focus on the binomial and normal distributions.

5.1 COMPUTING PROBABILITIES WITH THE BINOMIAL DISTRIBUTION

In Chapter 5 of the textbook, we discussed the binomial distribution model and computed probabilities using the binomial distribution model:

$$P(x \text{ successes}) = \frac{n!}{x!(n-x)!} p^x (1-p)^{n-x}$$

where n denotes the number of times the application or process is repeated (sometimes called the number of trials), x denotes the number of successes (out of n) of interest, and p is the probability of success for any individual.

To use the binomial distribution model, we need to specify n, p, and x. Excel has a probability function to compute probabilities from a binomial distribution. The function is "=BINOMDIST(x, n, p, $cumulative$)". The inputs for the function are the same as those we used in computing probabilities by hand with the binomial distribtion model (i.e., x, n, and p). Excel requires one additional input, labeled *cumulative*. The last entry in the BINOMDIST function is a logical value (i.e., one whose responses are true or false). We essentially use the cumulative distribution function by specifying "true" or do not use the cumulative distribution function by specifying "false." The cumulative distribution function returns the probability of observing x or fewer successes. For example, if we specify "true" and indicate $x = 5$ in the function, then Excel computes $P(X \le 5)$. In contrast, if we specify "false" and indicate $x = 5$ in the function, then Excel computes $P(X = 5)$. We illustrate the use of the function in the following example.

Example 5.1. In Example 5.9 in the textbook, we presented an example assessing the extent to which adults with allergies report relief from allergic symptoms with a specific medication. We know that the medication is effective in 80% of patients with allergies. If we provide the medication to 10 patients with allergies, what is the probability that it is effective in exactly 7?

For this example, $n = 10$, $p = 0.80$, and $x = 7$. We now use Excel to compute the desired probability. In Figure 5-1, we enter n, p, and x into an Excel worksheet. We now wish to compute the probability of 7 successes when $n = 10$ and the probability of success for any individual is 0.80. We use the BINOMDIST function and specify the cell locations for x (A2), n (B2), and p (C2). Because we want to compute the probability

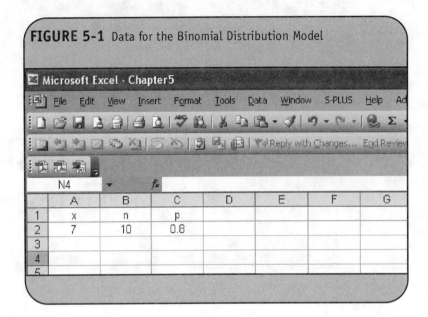

FIGURE 5-1 Data for the Binomial Distribution Model

of exactly 7 successes, we set *cumulative* = false. The specification of the formula is shown in Figure 5-2.

Once we enter these values, the probability is computed. The result is shown in Figure 5-3. We can also compute the probability of observing 7 or fewer successes by specifying *cumulative* = true in the function call. This is shown in Figure 5-4. The result is shown in Figure 5-5.

Thus, P(X = 7) = 0.201 and P($X \leq$ 7) = 0.322. In Figure 5-6, we entered all possible values of x for n = 10 (i.e., 0 through 10) and computed the probability of exactly x successes, as well as the probability of observing x successes or fewer using

the BINOMDIST function with *cumulative* = false and *cumulative* = true, respectively. Notice that some of the probabilities are very small—e.g., P(X = 0) = 1.024E − 07 = 0.0000001024—and also the relationship between the individual and cumulative probabilities.

5.2 COMPUTING PROBABILITIES WITH THE NORMAL DISTRIBUTION

In Chapter 5 of the textbook, we presented the normal distribution and showed how to compute probabilities using the standard normal distribution (z) and Table 1 in the

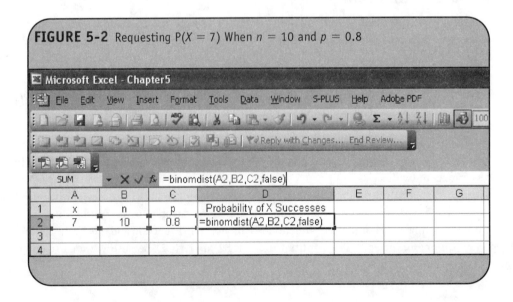

FIGURE 5-2 Requesting P(X = 7) When n = 10 and p = 0.8

FIGURE 5-3 P($X = 7$) When $n = 10$ and $p = 0.8$

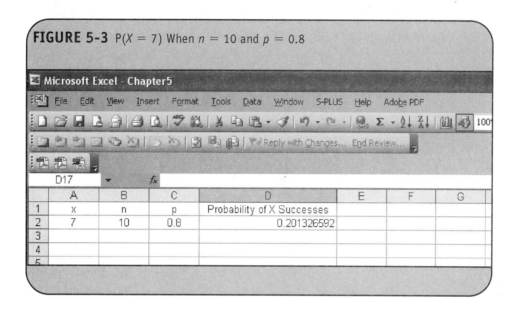

FIGURE 5-4 Requesting P($X \leq 7$) When $n = 10$ and $p = 0.8$

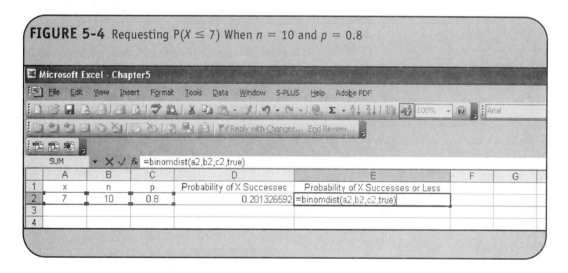

FIGURE 5-5 P($X \leq 7$) When $n = 10$ and $p = 0.8$

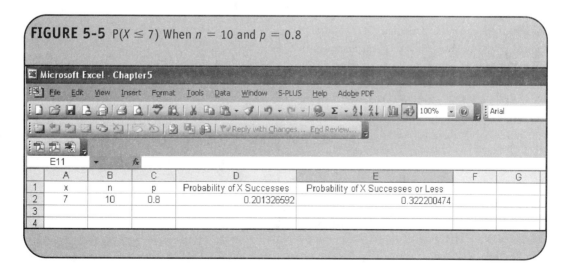

FIGURE 5-6 Binomial Probability Distribution for $n = 10$ and $p = 0.8$

Microsoft Excel - Chapter5

K26

	A	B	C	D	E	F	G
1	x	n	p	Probability of X Successes	Probability of X Successes or Less		
2	0	10	0.8	1.024E-07	1.024E-07		
3	1	10	0.8	0.000004096	4.1984E-06		
4	2	10	0.8	7.3728E-05	7.79264E-05		
5	3	10	0.8	0.000786432	0.000864358		
6	4	10	0.8	0.005505024	0.006369382		
7	5	10	0.8	0.026424115	0.032793498		
8	6	10	0.8	0.088080384	0.120873882		
9	7	10	0.8	0.201326592	0.322200474		
10	8	10	0.8	0.301989888	0.624190362		
11	9	10	0.8	0.268435456	0.892625818		
12	10	10	0.8	0.107374182	1		
13							
14							

Appendix of the textbook. Here we use Excel to compute probabilities for variables that are assumed to follow a normal distribution.

Excel has two probability functions to compute probabilities from normal distributions. The first computes probabilities from the standard normal distribution and the function is "=NORMSDIST(z)". The input for the function is the z value. The function returns the probability of observing a value from the standard normal distribution less than or equal to z (i.e., Excel returns the area under the standard normal curve to the left of or less than or equal to z). Figure 5-7 displays a worksheet with various values of z entered in column A. The NORMSDIST function is used in column B to generate probabilities less than z. For example, in cell B2 we enter "=NORMSDIST(A2)".

Recall that zero is the mean (and median) of the standard normal distribution, and thus $P(z \leq 0) = 0.5$. (Recall that for the normal distribution that $P(z \leq 0) = P(z < 0) = 0.5$.) In addition, the standard deviation is 1, so $P(-1 < z < 1) = P(z < 1) - P(z < -1) = 0.841 - 0.159 = 0.682$ (68% of the observations in a normal distribution fall between the mean minus one standard deviation and the mean plus one standard deviation).

In most applications, we analyze distributions that are normal with mean μ and standard deviation σ (which are not 0 and 1, respectively). Excel has a second function that computes probabilities from any normal distribution and the function is "=NORMDIST(x, μ, σ, *cumulative*)". The inputs for the function are the x value, the mean (μ), and standard deviation (σ) of the normal distribution and a logical value labeled *cumulative*. For almost all applications, we will use the cumulative distribution function by specifying "true." This will return the probability of observing a value from the normal distribution with specified mean and standard deviation less than or equal to x (i.e., Excel returns the area under the standard normal curve to the left of or less than or equal to x). If we specify cumulative as "false," the function will return the probability of x. Figure 5-8 displays a worksheet with x entered

FIGURE 5-7 Probabilities From the Standard Normal Distribution

Microsoft Excel - Chapter5

B7 =NORMSDIST(A7)

	A	B	C	D	E
1	Z	Probability Less than Z			
2	0	0.5			
3	1	0.841344746			
4	-1	0.158655254			
5	2	0.977249868			
6	-2	0.022750132			
7	3	0.998650102			
8					
9					

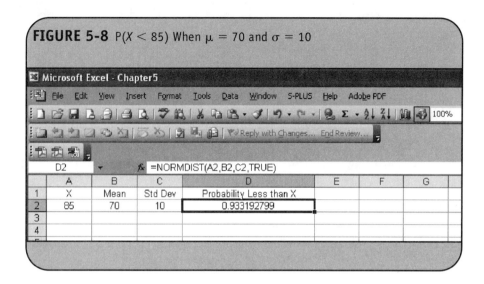

FIGURE 5-8 $P(X < 85)$ When $\mu = 70$ and $\sigma = 10$

in column A. We specify the mean and standard deviation of the distribution in column B and column C, respectively, and use the NORMDIST function to generate probabilities less than or equal to x. For example, in cell D2 we enter "=NORMDIST(A2,B2,C2,true)". For a normal distribution with $\mu = 70$ and standard $\sigma = 10$, $P(X < 85) = 0.9332$.

Example 5.2. In Example 5.11 in the textbook, we analyzed body mass index (BMI), which is assumed to be normally distributed for specific gender and age groups. The mean BMI for men aged 60 is 29 with a standard deviation of 6, and for women aged 60 the mean is 28 with a standard deviation of 7.

For men aged 60, we now use Excel to compute the following: $P(X < 35)$, $P(X < 41)$, and $P(X < 30)$. The results are shown in Figure 5-9. Suppose we now wish to compute the probability that a male has a BMI between 30 and 35—i.e., $P(30 < X < 35)$. This can be done using the NORMDIST function to compute the probabilities that a male has BMI less than 35 and less than 30 (as in Figure 5-9) and subtracting (Figure 5-10). The desired probability is computed by subtraction: $P(30 < X < 35) = P(X < 35) - P(X < 30) = 0.275$.

Now consider BMI in women. What is the probability that a female aged 60 has a BMI less than 30, and less than 35? What is the probability that a female aged 60 has a BMI between 30 and 35? We use the same approach but recall for women aged 60, the mean is 28 and the standard deviation is 7. The results are shown in Figure 5-11.

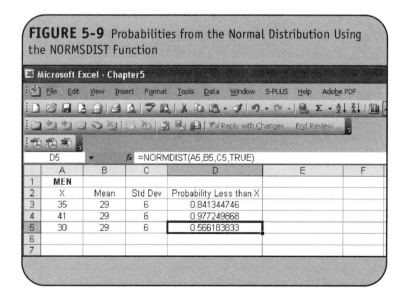

FIGURE 5-9 Probabilities from the Normal Distribution Using the NORMSDIST Function

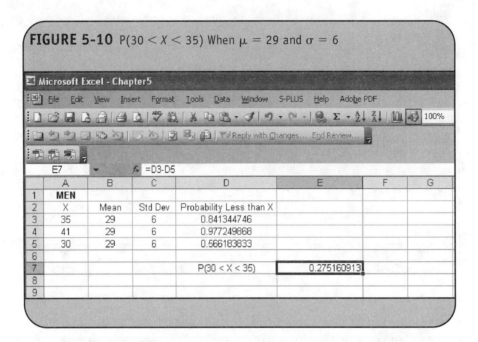

FIGURE 5-10 $P(30 < X < 35)$ When $\mu = 29$ and $\sigma = 6$

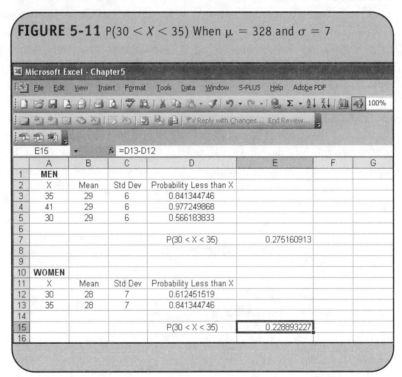

FIGURE 5-11 $P(30 < X < 35)$ When $\mu = 328$ and $\sigma = 7$

5.3   FINDING PERCENTILES OF THE NORMAL DISTRIBUTION

Excel can also be used to compute percentiles for the standard normal and for any normal distribution. The two functions are NORMSINV and NORMINV, respectively. The inputs for the functions are shown in the following text. Recall from Chapter 5 in the textbook that a percentile is a score that holds a specified percentage or proportion of scores below it. For example, the 80th percentile is the score that holds 80% of the scores below it.

The function to compute percentiles for the standard normal distribution is "=NORMSINV(*probability*)". The input for the function is the desired percentile, entered as a probability or proportion. For example, to compute the 80th or 95th percentiles, we specify 0.80 or 0.95, respectively.

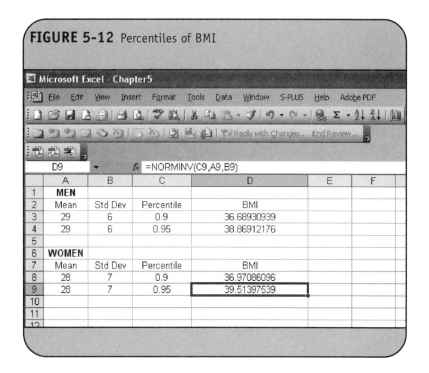

FIGURE 5-12 Percentiles of BMI

The function to compute percentiles for any normal distribution is "=NORMINV(*probability*, μ, σ)". The inputs for the function are the desired percentile entered as a probability, the mean (μ), and standard deviation (σ) of the normal distribution.

Example 5.3. Using the data in Example 5.2, we now use Excel to compute the 90th and 95th percentiles of BMI for men and women. The results are shown in Figure 5-12. In men, 90% of BMIs are below 36.7 and 95% are below 38.9. In women, 90% of BMIs are below 37.0 and 95% are below 39.5.

5.4 PRACTICE PROBLEMS

1. Total cholesterol in children aged 10 to 15 years of age is assumed to follow a normal distribution with a mean of 191 and a standard deviation of 22.4.
    a. What proportion of children 10 to 15 years of age have total cholesterol between 180 and 190?
    b. What proportion of children 10 to 15 years of age would be classified as hyperlipidemic (assume that hyperlipidemia is defined as a total cholesterol level over 200)?
    c. What is the 90th percentile of total cholesterol?
2. Among coffee drinkers, men drink a mean of 3.2 cups per day with a standard deviation of 0.8 cups. Assume the number of coffee drinks per day follows a normal distribution.
    a. What proportion drink 2 cups per day or more?
    b. What proportion drink no more than 4 cups per day?

    c. If the top 5% of coffee drinkers are considered heavy coffee drinkers, what is the minimum number of cups consumed by a heavy coffee drinker? (*Hint*: Find the 95th percentile.)
3. A study is conducted to assess the impact of caffeine consumption, smoking, alcohol consumption, and physical activity on the risk of cardiovascular disease. Suppose that 40% of participants consume caffeine and smoke. If 8 participants are evaluated, what is the probability that:
    a. Exactly half of them consume caffeine and smoke?
    b. At most 6 consume caffeine and smoke?
4. A recent study of cardiovascular risk factors reports that 30% of adults meet the criteria for hypertension. If 15 adults are assessed, what is the probability that:
    a. Exactly 5 meet the criteria for hypertension?
    b. None meet the criteria for hypertension?
    c. Less than or equal to 7 meet the criteria for hypertension?
5. Diastolic blood pressures are assumed to follow a normal distribution with a mean of 85 and a standard deviation of 12.
    a. What proportion of people have diastolic blood pressures less than 90?
    b. What proportion have diastolic blood pressures between 80 and 90?
    c. If someone has a diastolic blood pressure of 100, what percentile does this represent?

Confidence Interval Estimates

In Chapter 6 of the textbook, we presented formulas to generate confidence intervals for means (μ) and proportions (p) in one sample and for differences in means ($\mu_1 - \mu_2$) and differences in proportions ($p_1 - p_2$) in two independent samples. We also discussed confidence intervals for the mean difference (μ_d) when two samples were matched or paired. For each application, we used the same general approach. Confidence intervals for each parameter take the following form:

Point estimate $\pm$ Margin of error

The point estimate depends on the parameter being estimated. For example, when estimating the mean of a population, μ, the point estimate is the sample mean, $\overline{X}$. When estimating the population proportion, p, the point estimate is the sample proportion, $\hat{p}$. The margin of error includes two components. The first component is from a probability distribution (e.g., z or t) and reflects the selected confidence level (e.g., 90%, 95%) and the second component is the standard error of the point estimate. For example, the standard error of the sample mean, $\overline{X}$, is SE $= {}^s\!/\!\sqrt{n}$. The standard error of the sample proportion, $\hat{p}$, is SE $= \sqrt{\hat{p}(1-\hat{p})/n}$.

In Chapter 6 of the textbook, we presented formulas for confidence intervals for various parameters (see Table 6-22 in Section 6.7 of the textbook for details). Here we use Excel to generate confidence intervals for various parameters. Excel does not generate confidence intervals directly; instead, we use specific Excel functions to produce the z or t values that reflect the desired confidence level and then construct the confidence interval.

6.1   CONFIDENCE INTERVALS FOR ONE SAMPLE, CONTINUOUS OUTCOME

In Chapter 6 of the textbook, we presented the following formulas for confidence intervals for the mean of a continuous variable in one sample.

$$n > 30 \ \ \overline{X} \pm z \frac{s}{\sqrt{n}} \ \text{(Find } z \text{ in Table 1B)}$$

$$n < 30 \ \ \overline{X} \pm t \frac{s}{\sqrt{n}} \ \text{(Find } t \text{ in Table 2, } df = n - 1\text{)}$$

When computing the confidence intervals by hand, we computed the sample size, mean, and standard deviation and then used Table 1B or Table 2 in the Appendix of the textbook to find the appropriate z or t value to reflect the desired confidence level. Here we use Excel to compute summary statistics and to determine the appropriate z or t value for the confidence interval. Once all of the requisite components are determined, we construct the confidence interval.

Excel has a function that computes z values that can be used in confidence intervals. The function is "=NORMSINV (*lower tail area*)". To use this function for confidence intervals, we specify the area under the curve in the lower tail of the standard normal distribution. For example, for a 95% confidence interval, the area in the lower tail is 0.975. Figure 6-1 shows the standard normal distribution, z, and the z values that hold the middle 95% of the distribution, $P(-1.96 < X < 1.96) = 0.95$.

To use the NORMSINV function for confidence intervals, we specify the probability in the *lower tail* of the standard

FIGURE 6-1

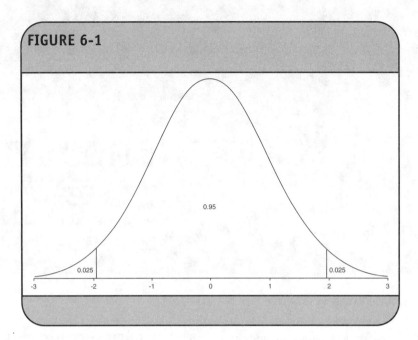

normal distribution. To produce the *z* value for a 95% confidence interval, we specify "=NORMSINV(0.975)", which returns 1.96.

Excel has a second function that computes *t* values that can be used in confidence intervals. The function is "=TINV(*total tail area, df*)." To use this function for confidence intervals, we specify the *total area* in the tail of the *t* distribution along with degrees of freedom, df. For a 95% confidence interval, the total tail area is 0.05 and for one sample, the degrees of freedom are df = *n* − 1. We now illustrate the use of these formulas to compute confidence intervals.

Example 6.1. In Example 6.1 in the textbook, we analyzed data on *n* = 3539 participants who attended the seventh examination of the Offspring in the Framingham Heart Study. Descriptive statistics on variables measured in the sample are shown in Table 6-1. We will use Excel to generate 95% confidence intervals for each characteristic. Because the sample size is large, we use the confidence interval formula with *z* as opposed to *t*. The data are entered into an Excel worksheet as shown in Figure 6-2.

First, we compute the standard errors for each characteristic as SE = $s/\sqrt{n}$ and place these values in column E. For systolic blood pressure, the following is entered into cell E2: "=D2/SQRT(B2)". We then compute the *z* scores for 95% confidence intervals and place these in column F. The computation is the same for each characteristic—for example, in cell F2 we enter "=NORMSINV(0.975)". The standard errors and *z* values are shown in Figure 6-3.

Note that had we wanted 90% confidence intervals, we would have specified "=NORMSINV(0.95)" in column F.

We now compute the lower and upper limits of the 95% confidence intervals using $\overline{X} \pm z \dfrac{s}{\sqrt{n}}$. For systolic blood pressure, the lower limit is "=C2 − (F2*E2)" and the upper limit is "=C2 + (F2*E2)". (The product of the *z* value and the standard error produce the margin of error.) The confidence intervals are shown in Figure 6-4.

Example 6.2. In Example 6.2 in the textbook, we presented data on a subsample of *n* = 10 participants who attended the seventh examination of the Framingham Offspring Study. Descriptive statistics on variables measured in the subsample are shown in Table 6-2.

We will use Excel to generate 95% confidence intervals for each characteristic. Because the sample size is small, we use the confidence interval formula with *t* as opposed to *z*. The data are entered into an Excel worksheet as shown in Figure 6-5.

First we compute the standard errors for each characteristic as SE = $s/\sqrt{n}$ and place these values in column E—e.g., for

TABLE 6-1 Descriptive Statistics, Framingham Heart Study Offspring

Characteristic	*n*	Mean ($\overline{X}$)	Standard Deviation (*s*)
Systolic blood pressure	3534	127.3	19.0
Diastolic blood pressure	3532	74.0	9.9
Total serum cholesterol	3310	200.3	36.8
Weight (lb)	3506	174.4	38.7
Height (in)	3326	65.957	3.749
Body mass index (BMI)	3326	28.15	5.32

FIGURE 6-2 Data From Framingham Study

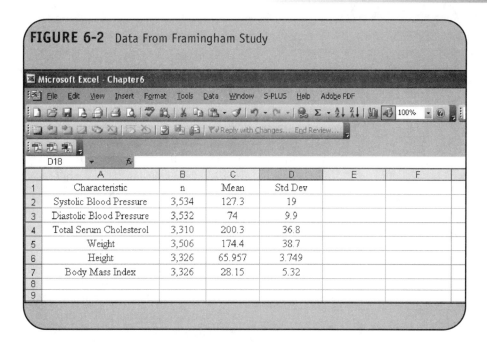

FIGURE 6-3 Standard Errors and *z* Values for Confidence Intervals

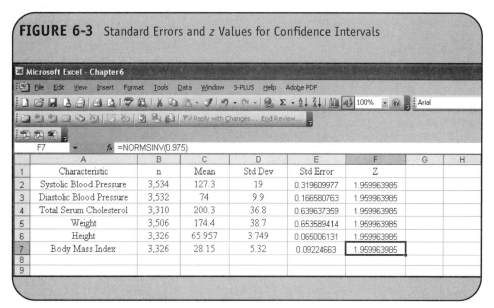

FIGURE 6-4 Upper and Lower Limits of 95% Confidence Intervals

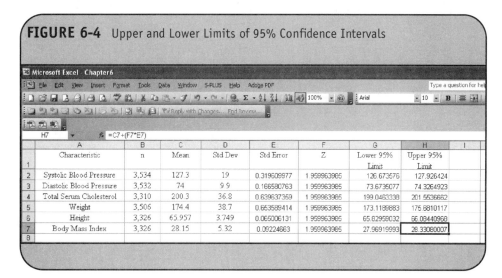

TABLE 6-2 Descriptive Statistics, Framingham Heart Study Offspring Subsample

Characteristic	n	Mean ($\overline{X}$)	Standard Deviation (s)
Systolic blood pressure	10	121.2	11.1
Diastolic blood pressure	10	71.3	7.2
Total serum cholesterol	10	202.3	37.7
Weight (lb)	10	176.0	33.0
Height (in)	10	67.175	4.205
Body mass index (BMI)	10	27.26	3.10

Example 6.3. In Example 4.3 in the textbook, we presented data on the subset of $n = 10$ participants, which were summarized in Example 6-2. The data values were presented in Table 4-12 of the textbook and are shown in Table 6-3. The data are entered into an Excel worksheet and shown in Figure 6-8.

In Chapter 4 of the Excel workbook, we described the Data Analysis ToolPak and generated summary statistics on continuous variables using the Descriptive Statistics Analysis Tool. This tool can be used to generate summary statistics and also to generate information that can be used to produce a confidence interval. Suppose we wish to generate descriptive statistics on systolic blood pressures (SBP). Using the Data Analysis ToolPak and selecting the Descriptive Statistics Module produces the dialog box shown in Figure 6-9.

In the dialog box, we specify the range of the data, we request that the results be placed in a new worksheet entitled *Descriptives on SBP*, we request summary statistics, and confidence interval information for a 95% confidence level. In the "Confidence Level for Means" box, any level from 0% to 100% can be specified (typical values are 90%, 95%, and 99%). The information in the new worksheet *Descriptives on SBP* is shown in Figure 6-10.

The information in cell B16 is the margin of error (i.e., the product of the t value for 95% confidence and the standard error). We must now take the margin of error and add it to and subtract it from the sample mean (point estimate) to produce the confidence limits. This is done and shown in Figure 6-11. Notice that the confidence limits shown in Figure 6-11 are identical to those shown in Figure 6-7.

systolic blood pressure, the following is entered into cell E2: "=D2/SQRT(B2)". We then compute the t scores for 95% confidence intervals and place these in column F. The computation is the same for each characteristic—for example, in cell F2 we enter "=TINV(0.05,B2−1)". The standard errors and t values are shown in Figure 6-6.

We now compute the lower and upper limits of the 95% confidence intervals using $\overline{X} \pm t\dfrac{s}{\sqrt{n}}$. For systolic blood pressure, the lower limit is "=C2 − (F2*E2)" and the upper limit is "=C2 + (F2*E2)". The confidence intervals are shown in Figure 6-7.

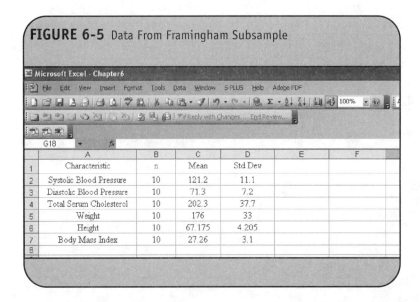

FIGURE 6-5 Data From Framingham Subsample

FIGURE 6-6 Standard Errors and *t* Values for Confidence Intervals

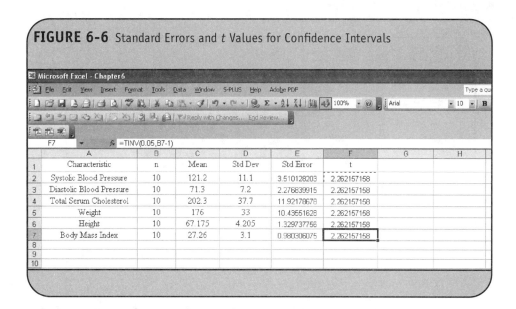

FIGURE 6-7 Upper and Lower Limits of 95% Confidence Intervals

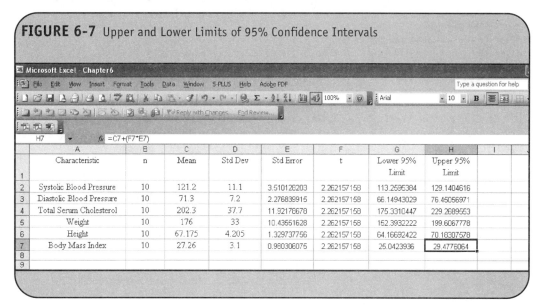

TABLE 6-3 Subsample of *n* = 10 Participants Attending the Seventh Examination of the Framingham Offspring Study

Participant ID	Systolic Blood Pressure	Diastolic Blood Pressure	Total Serum Cholesterol	Weight (lb)	Height (in)	BMI
1	141	76	199	138	63.00	24.4
2	119	64	150	183	69.75	26.4
3	122	62	227	153	65.75	24.9
4	127	81	227	178	70.00	25.5
5	125	70	163	161	70.50	22.8
6	123	72	210	206	70.00	29.6
7	105	81	205	235	72.00	31.9
8	113	63	275	151	60.75	28.8
9	106	67	208	213	69.00	31.5
10	131	77	159	142	61.00	26.8

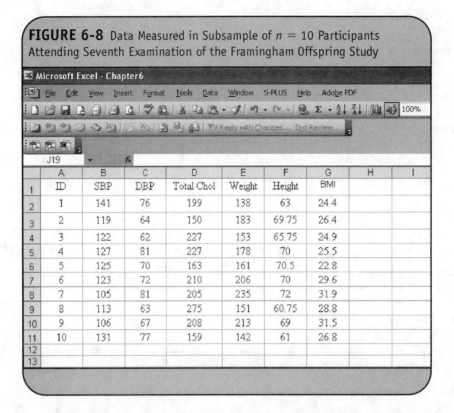

FIGURE 6-8 Data Measured in Subsample of $n = 10$ Participants Attending Seventh Examination of the Framingham Offspring Study

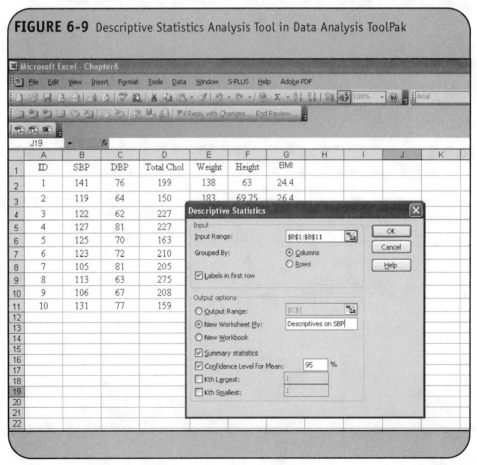

FIGURE 6-9 Descriptive Statistics Analysis Tool in Data Analysis ToolPak

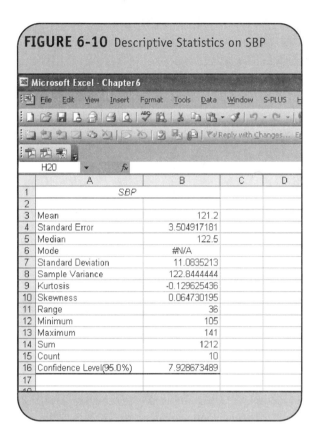

FIGURE 6-10 Descriptive Statistics on SBP

6.2   CONFIDENCE INTERVALS FOR ONE SAMPLE, DICHOTOMOUS OUTCOME

In Chapter 6 of the textbook, we presented the following formula for the confidence interval for a proportion (of dichotomous variable) in one sample:

$$\hat{p} \pm z\sqrt{\frac{\hat{p}(1-\hat{p})}{n}} \quad \text{(Find } z \text{ in Table 1B)}$$

When computing the confidence intervals by hand, we computed the sample size and sample proportion and then used Table 1B in the Appendix of the textbook to find the appropriate z value to reflect the desired confidence level. We now use Excel to compute the sample proportion and to determine the appropriate z value for the confidence interval.

Example 6.4. In Example 6.4 in the textbook, we analyzed data on the prevalence of cardiovascular disease (CVD) measured in men and women at the fifth examination of the Framingham Offspring Study. The data are shown in Table 6-4. The data are entered into an Excel worksheet and shown in Figure 6-12.

In Figure 6-13, we compute the sample proportions with prevalent CVD by dividing the numbers with prevalent CVD by the respective totals and then generate the z values for 95%

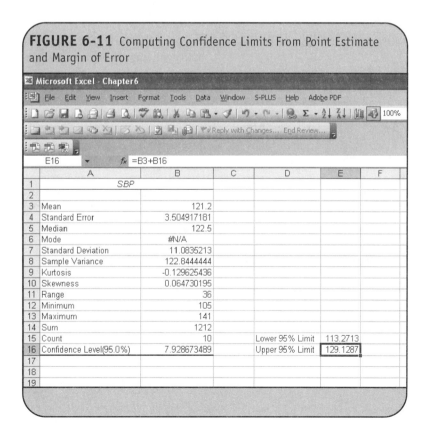

FIGURE 6-11 Computing Confidence Limits From Point Estimate and Margin of Error

TABLE 6-4 Prevalence of CVD in Men and Women Attending the Fifth Examination of the Framingham Offspring Study

	Free of CVD	Prevalent CVD	Total
Men	1548	244	1792
Women	1872	135	2007
Total	3420	379	3799

confidence using the NORMSINV function. The sample proportions and z values are shown in Figure 6-13.

In Figure 6-14, we compute the upper and lower limits of the 95% confidence interval using $p \pm z \sqrt{\dfrac{p(1-p)}{n}}$. Notice how the formula is implemented. For example, the lower 95% confidence limit for the total sample is in cell G4 and is computed as "=E4−F4*SQRT(E4*(1−E4)/D4)". The upper 95% confidence limit for the total sample is in cell H4 and is computed as "=E4+F4*SQRT(E4*(1−E4)/D4)".

6.3   CONFIDENCE INTERVALS FOR TWO INDEPENDENT SAMPLES, CONTINUOUS OUTCOME

In Chapter 6 of the textbook, we presented the following formulas for confidence intervals for the difference in means of a continuous variable in two independent samples:

$n_1 \geq 30$ and $n_2 \geq 30$

$$(\overline{X}_1 - \overline{X}_2) \pm z S_p \sqrt{\frac{1}{n_1} + \frac{1}{n_2}} \text{ (Find } z \text{ in Table 1B)}$$

$$n_1 < 30 \text{ or } n_2 < 30 \ (\overline{X}_1 - \overline{X}_2) \pm t S_p \sqrt{\frac{1}{n_1} + \frac{1}{n_2}}$$

$$\text{(Find } t \text{ in Table 2, } df = n_1 + n_2 - 2)$$

where

$$S_p = \sqrt{\frac{(n_1-1)s_1^2 + (n_2-1)s_2^2}{n_1 + n_2 - 2}}$$

When computing the confidence intervals by hand, we computed the sample sizes, means, and standard deviations in each sample. We then computed the pooled estimate of the common standard deviation, S_p, and used Table 1B or Table 2 in the Appendix of the textbook to find the appropriate z or t value to reflect the desired confidence level. We now use Excel to compute summary statistics and to determine the appropriate z or t value for the confidence interval. Once all of the requisite components are determined, we construct the confidence interval.

Example 6.5. In Example 6.5 in the textbook, we analyzed data on $n = 3539$ participants who attended the seventh examination of the Offspring in the Framingham Heart Study and compared men and women on the characteristics shown in Table 6-5.

We will use Excel to generate 95% confidence intervals for the difference in means between men and women. Because the sample sizes are large, we use the confidence interval formula with z as opposed to t. The data are entered into an Excel worksheet as shown in Figure 6-15.

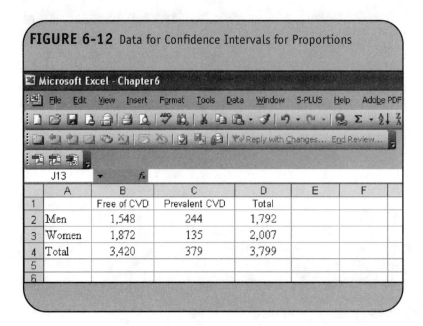

FIGURE 6-12 Data for Confidence Intervals for Proportions

FIGURE 6-13 Sample Proportion and *z* Values for Confidence Intervals

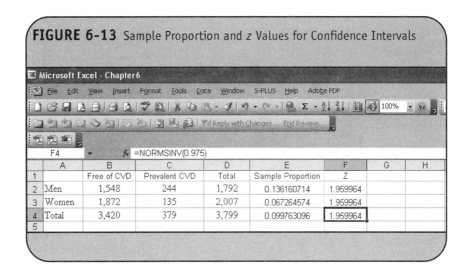

FIGURE 6-14 Upper and Lower Limits of 95% Confidence Intervals

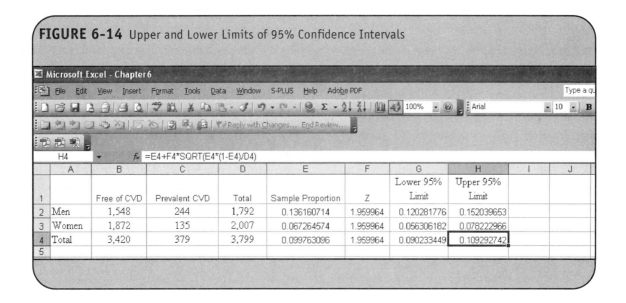

TABLE 6-5 Characteristics Measured in Men and Women Attending the Seventh Examination of the Framingham Heart Study

Characteristic	Men			Women		
	N	$\overline{X}$	*s*	*n*	$\overline{X}$	*s*
Systolic blood pressure	1623	128.2	17.5	1911	126.5	20.1
Diastolic blood pressure	1622	75.6	9.8	1910	72.6	9.7
Total serum cholesterol	1544	192.4	35.2	1766	207.1	36.7
Weight (lb)	1612	194.0	33.8	1894	157.7	34.6
Height (in)	1545	68.9	2.7	1781	63.4	2.5
Body mass index (BMI)	1545	28.8	4.6	1781	27.6	5.9

FIGURE 6-15 Data for Confidence Intervals for Differences in Means

First we compute the pooled estimates of the common standard deviations $S_p = \sqrt{\dfrac{(n_1-1)s_1^2 + (n_2-1)s_2^2}{n_1 + n_2 - 2}}$ and place these in column H. For systolic blood pressure, the following is entered into cell H3: "=SQRT(((B3−1)*D3^2 + (E3−1)*G3^2)/(B3+E3−2))". We then compute the z scores for 95% confidence intervals and place these in column I. The computation is the same for each characteristic—for example, in cell I3 we enter "=NORMSINV(0.975)". The pooled

estimates of the common standard deviations and z values are shown in Figure 6-16.

We now compute the point estimates for the difference in means $(\overline{X}_1 - \overline{X}_2)$ and the lower and upper limits of the 95% confidence intervals using $(\overline{X}_1 - \overline{X}_2) \pm z\, S_p \sqrt{\dfrac{1}{n_1} + \dfrac{1}{n_2}}$. The confidence intervals are shown in Figure 6-17.

The 95% confidence limits are shown in column K and column L for each characteristic. The same approach is used to

FIGURE 6-16 S_p and z Values for Confidence Intervals

FIGURE 6-17 Upper and Lower Limits of 95% Confidence Intervals

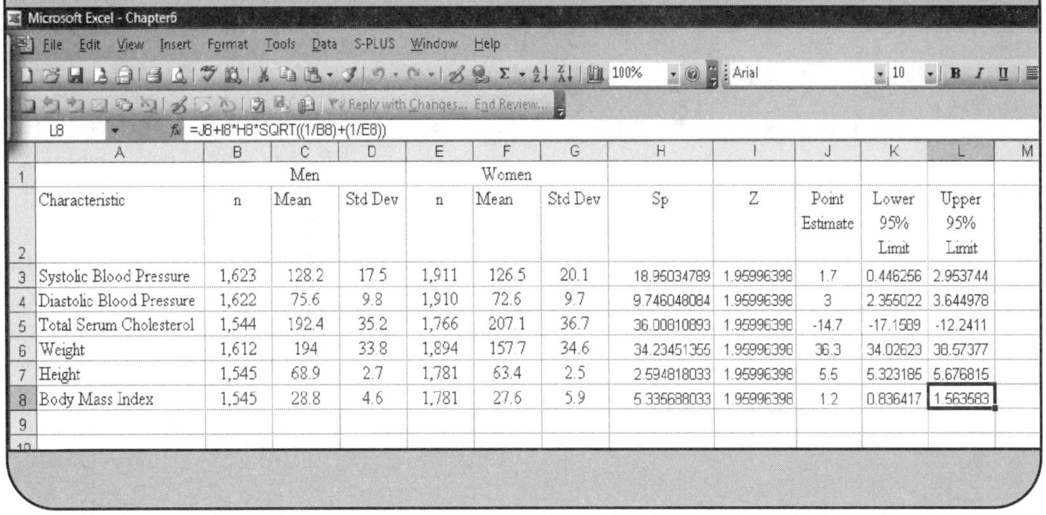

	A	B	C	D	E	F	G	H	I	J	K	L
1			Men			Women						
2	Characteristic	n	Mean	Std Dev	n	Mean	Std Dev	Sp	Z	Point Estimate	Lower 95% Limit	Upper 95% Limit
3	Systolic Blood Pressure	1,623	128.2	17.5	1,911	126.5	20.1	18.95034789	1.95996398	1.7	0.446256	2.953744
4	Diastolic Blood Pressure	1,622	75.6	9.8	1,910	72.6	9.7	9.746048084	1.95996398	3	2.355022	3.644978
5	Total Serum Cholesterol	1,544	192.4	35.2	1,766	207.1	36.7	36.00810893	1.95996398	-14.7	-17.1589	-12.2411
6	Weight	1,612	194	33.8	1,894	157.7	34.6	34.23451355	1.95996398	36.3	34.02623	38.57377
7	Height	1,545	68.9	2.7	1,781	63.4	2.5	2.594818033	1.95996398	5.5	5.323185	5.676815
8	Body Mass Index	1,545	28.8	4.6	1,781	27.6	5.9	5.335688033	1.95996398	1.2	0.836417	1.563583
9												

compute confidence intervals for the difference in means when the sample sizes are small (i.e., when one or both of the sample sizes are less than 30), except that the TINV function is used to compute the appropriate value from the t distribution with degrees of freedom equal to $n_1 + n_2 - 2$.

6.4 CONFIDENCE INTERVALS FOR MATCHED SAMPLES, CONTINUOUS OUTCOME

In Chapter 6 of the textbook, we presented the following formulas for confidence intervals for the mean difference of a continuous variable in two dependent or matched samples.

$$n > 30 \quad \overline{X}_d \pm z\frac{s_d}{\sqrt{n}} \text{ (Find } z \text{ in Table 1B)}$$

$$n < 30 \quad \overline{X}_d \pm t\frac{s_d}{\sqrt{n}} \text{ (Find } t \text{ in Table 2, } df = n - 1)$$

where n is the number of participants or pairs and $\overline{X}_d$ and s_d are the mean and standard deviation of the difference scores (where differences are computed on each participant or between members of a matched pair).

We now use Excel to compute summary statistics and to determine the appropriate z or t value for the confidence interval. Once all of the requisite components are determined, we will construct the confidence interval.

Example 6.6. In Example 6.7 in the textbook, we analyzed systolic blood pressures measured at the sixth and seventh examinations of the Offspring in the Framingham Heart Study in a subsample of $n = 15$ randomly selected participants. The data are shown in Table 6-6.

We use Excel to compute difference scores, to generate summary statistics on the difference scores, and to generate a 95% confidence interval for the mean difference in systolic blood pressures over time. The data are entered into an Excel worksheet as shown in Figure 6-18. Difference scores are

TABLE 6-6 Systolic Blood Pressures Measured at Examinations 6 and 7

Subject Identification Number	Examination 6	Examination 7
1	168	141
2	111	119
3	139	122
4	127	127
5	155	125
6	115	123
7	125	113
8	123	106
9	130	131
10	137	142
11	130	131
12	129	135
13	112	119
14	141	130
15	122	121

FIGURE 6-18 Data for Confidence Interval for Mean Difference

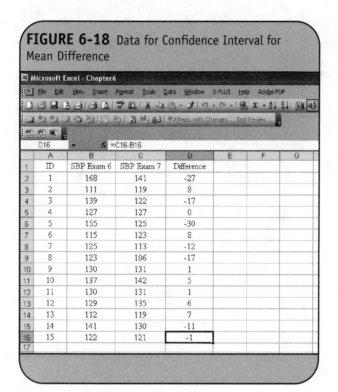

computed for each participant by subtracting the systolic blood pressure measured at Exam 6 from that measured at Exam 7.

We next use the Descriptive Statistics Analysis Tool to generate descriptive statistics on the differences and we request the confidence interval information. The specifications for the analysis are shown in Figure 6-19. In the following, we request that the results are placed in the current worksheet and we specify the top-left corner of the results table as cell F1. The descriptive statistics are shown in Figure 6-20.

Cell G16 contains the margin of error (i.e., the product of the t value for 95% confidence and the standard error). We now take the margin of error and add it to and subtract it from the mean difference in the sample (point estimate in cell G3) to produce the confidence limits. This is done and shown in Figure 6-21.

6.5   CONFIDENCE INTERVALS FOR TWO INDEPENDENT SAMPLES, DICHOTOMOUS OUTCOME

In Chapter 6 of the textbook, we presented the following formula for the confidence interval for a difference in proportions in two independent samples.

$$\hat{p}_1 - \hat{p}_2 \pm z\sqrt{\frac{\hat{p}_1(1-\hat{p}_1)}{n_1} + \frac{\hat{p}_2(1-\hat{p}_2)}{n_2}} \quad (\text{Find } z \text{ in Table 1B})$$

FIGURE 6-19 Computing the Confidence Interval on the Difference Scores

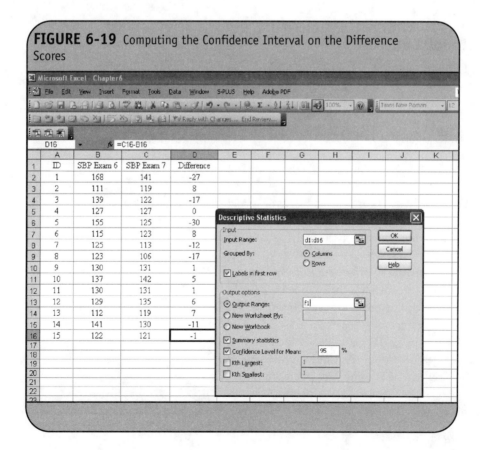

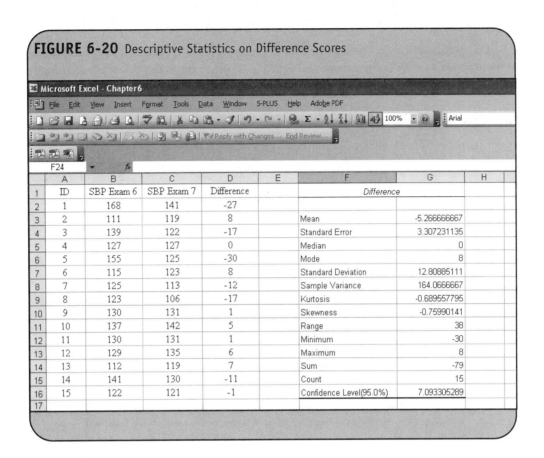

FIGURE 6-20 Descriptive Statistics on Difference Scores

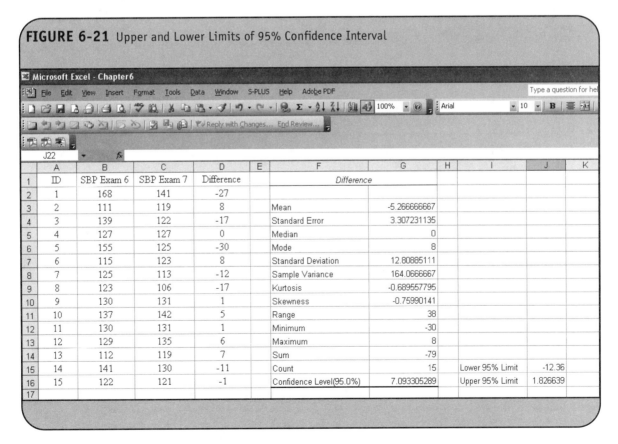

FIGURE 6-21 Upper and Lower Limits of 95% Confidence Interval

When computing the confidence intervals by hand, we computed the sample sizes and sample proportions, and then used Table 1B in the Appendix of the textbook to find the appropriate z value to reflect the desired confidence level. We now use Excel to compute the sample proportions and to determine the appropriate z value for the confidence interval.

Example 6.7. In Example 6.4 of the Excel workbook, we analyzed data on the prevalence of cardiovascular disease (CVD) measured in men and women at the fifth examination of the Framingham Offspring Study. The data are shown in Table 6-4. The data are entered into an Excel worksheet and shown in Figure 6-22.

In Figure 6-23, we compute the sample proportions with prevalent CVD by dividing the numbers with prevalent CVD by the respective totals. We then compute the point estimate as the difference in sample proportions and generate the z value for 95% confidence using the NORMSINV function.

In Figure 6-24, we compute the upper and lower limits of the 95% confidence interval using $\hat{p}_1 - \hat{p}_2 \pm \sqrt{\frac{\hat{p}_1(1-\hat{p}_1)}{n_1} + \frac{\hat{p}_2(1-\hat{p}_2)}{n_2}}$. Notice how the formula is implemented (see the formula for the upper limit in the formula bar). Excel can be used to generate confidence intervals for relative risks and odds ratios using a similar approach. The exact

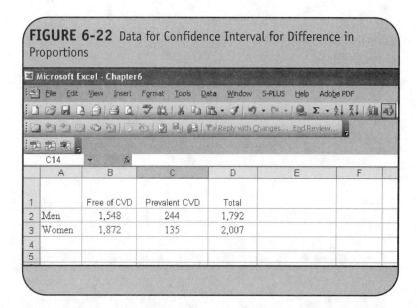

FIGURE 6-22 Data for Confidence Interval for Difference in Proportions

	Free of CVD	Prevalent CVD	Total
Men	1,548	244	1,792
Women	1,872	135	2,007

FIGURE 6-23 Sample Proportions, Difference in Proportions and z Value for Confidence Interval

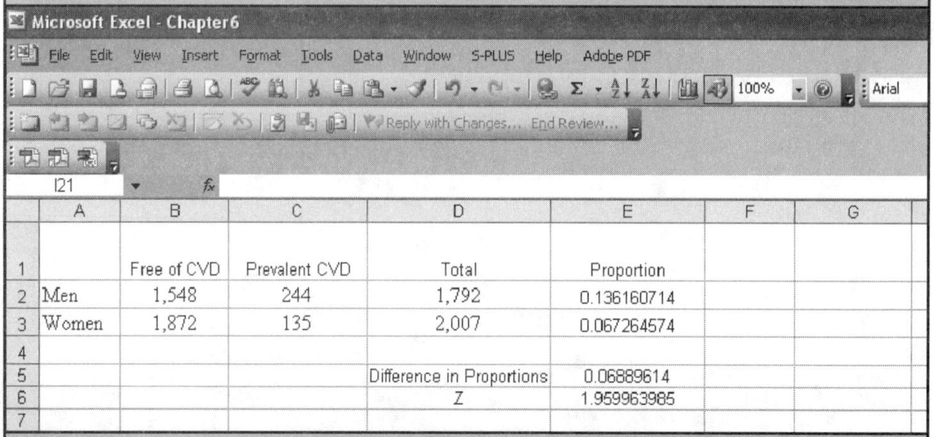

	Free of CVD	Prevalent CVD	Total	Proportion
Men	1,548	244	1,792	0.136160714
Women	1,872	135	2,007	0.067264574
			Difference in Proportions	0.06889614
			Z	1.959963985

FIGURE 6-24 Upper and Lower Limits of 95% Confidence Interval

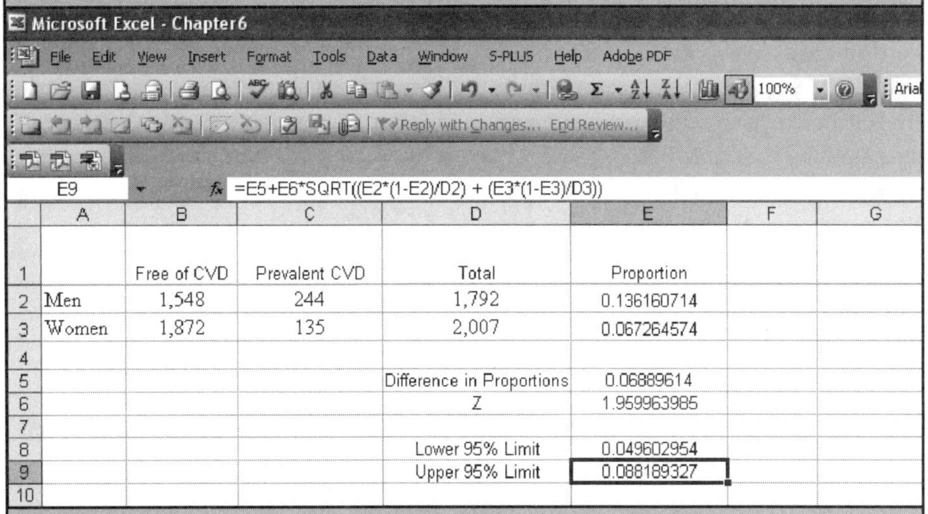

formulas for these confidence intervals can be found in Chapter 6 of the textbook.

6.6   PRACTICE PROBLEMS

1. A study is run to estimate the mean total cholesterol level in children 2 to 6 years of age. A sample of 9 participants is selected and their total cholesterol levels are measured as follows:

    185   225   240   196   175   180   194   147   223

    Generate a 95% confidence interval for the true mean total cholesterol levels in children.

2. A clinical trial is planned to compare an experimental medication designed to lower blood pressure to a placebo. Before starting the trial, a pilot study is conducted involving 10 participants. The objective of the study is to assess how systolic blood pressure changes untreated over time. Systolic blood pressures are measured at baseline and again 4 weeks later. Compute a 95% confidence interval for the mean difference in blood pressures over 4 weeks.

    Baseline: 120 145 130 160 152 143 126 121 115 135

    4 Weeks: 122 142 135 158 155 140 130 120 124 130

3. After the pilot study described in Problem 2, the main trial is conducted and involves a total of 200 patients. Patients are enrolled and randomized to receive either the experimental medication or the placebo. The data shown in Table 6-7 are data collected at the end of the study after 6 weeks on the assigned treatment. Generate a 95% confidence interval for the difference in proportions of patients with hypertension between groups.

4. The following data were collected as part of a study of coffee consumption among male and female undergraduate students. The following reflects cups per day consumed:

Male:	3	4	6	8	2	1	0	2
Female:	5	3	1	2	0	4	3	1

TABLE 6-7 Data for Problem 3

	Experimental (n = 100)	Placebo (n = 100)
% Hypertensive	14%	22%

Generate a 95% confidence interval for the difference in mean numbers of cups of coffee consumed between men and women.

5. A clinical trial is conducted comparing a new pain reliever for arthritis to a placebo. Participants are randomly assigned to receive the new treatment or a placebo. The outcome is pain relief within 30 minutes. The data are shown in Table 6-8.

a. Generate a 95% confidence interval for the proportion of patients on the new medication who report pain relief.

b. Generate a 95% confidence interval for the difference in proportions of patients who report pain relief.

TABLE 6-8 Data for Problem 5

	Pain Relief	No Pain Relief
New medication	44	76
Placebo	21	99

Hypothesis Testing Procedures

In Chapter 7 of the textbook, we presented the approach for hypothesis testing for means (μ) and proportions (p) in one sample, differences in means ($\mu_1 - \mu_2$) and differences in proportions ($p_1 - p_2$) in two independent samples, the mean difference in two dependent samples (μ_d), and for differences in means and proportions in more than two independent samples. For each test we used the same general five-step approach, which is outlined below:

- *Step 1:* Set up hypotheses (H_0 and H_1) and select a level of significance, α.
- *Step 2:* Choose the appropriate test statistic (e.g., z, t, F, χ^2).
- *Step 3:* Determine critical values and set up the decision rule (which depends on α, the test statistic, and whether the test is upper-, lower-, or two-tailed).
- *Step 4:* Compute the test statistic based on observed sample data.
- *Step 5:* Draw a conclusion by comparing the test statistic to the critical value.

The test statistic (Step 2) varies depending on the specific test. When we conducted tests of hypothesis by hand in Chapter 7 of the textbook, we ultimately drew a conclusion by comparing the test statistic to the critical value, which was derived from an appropriate probability distribution. There is an alternative means of drawing a conclusion and it involves comparing the p-value of a test (defined as the exact significance level) to the selected level of significance, α. The p-value is the probability of observing a test statistic as or more extreme than that observed and it can be one-sided or two-sided. For example, suppose we conduct an upper-tailed test for the population mean (i.e., $H_1: \mu > \mu_0$) and observe a test statistic $z = 2.04$. The p-value is $P(z \geq 2.04)$. If we conduct a two-sided test for the population mean (i.e., $H_1: \mu \neq \mu_0$) and observe a test statistic $z = 2.04$, the p-value is $P(z \geq 2.04) + P(z \leq -2.04) = 2 \times P(z \geq 2.04)$. We use Excel to compute the test statistics for each test and to compute p-values for each test to draw conclusions based on the following:

$$\text{Reject } H_0 \text{ if } p \leq \alpha.$$

p-values for tests involving z statistics are computed with the NORMSDIST function, and p-values for tests involving t statistics are computed with the TDIST function.

To compute p-values for tests involving a z statistic, we use the NORMSDIST function: "=NORMSDIST(z)". To use the NORMSDIST function, we specify the value of the test statistic, z. The function returns the area under the standard normal curve below z. To use the NORMSDIST function to compute p-values, we make the following modifications:

$$\text{One-sided } z \text{ test} = \text{"1}-\text{NORMSDIST(ABS}(z))\text{"}$$

$$\text{Two-sided } z \text{ test} = \text{"2*(1}-\text{NORMSDIST(ABS}(z)))\text{"}$$

The ABS function takes the absolute value of the test statistic. By using the ABS function, we can use the preceding one-sided formula for both upper- and lower-tailed tests.

To compute p-values for tests involving t statistics, we use the TDIST function: "=TDIST(t, df, $test\ type$)". To use the TDIST function, we specify the test statistic, t, the degrees of freedom (e.g., for a one sample test of means, df = $n - 1$), and then the *test type*. The *test type* indicates whether the test is one- or two-tailed (i.e., *test type* = 1 for upper- or lower-tailed tests and *test type* = 2 for two-tailed tests). The function returns the area in the t distribution in one or two tails (depending on the test type). The TDIST function is used as follows to compute *p*-values:

One-sided t test = "TDIST(ABS(t), df, 1)"

Two-sided t test = "TDIST(ABS(t), df, 2)"

Again, the ABS function is used to take the absolute value of the test statistic.

7.1 TESTS WITH ONE SAMPLE, CONTINUOUS OUTCOME

For a one-sample test of a hypothesis with a continuous outcome, the hypotheses are:

$$H_0: \mu = \mu_0$$

$$H_1: \mu > \mu_0 \quad H_1: \mu < \mu_0 \text{ or } H_1: \mu \neq \mu_0$$

where μ is the mean of the population of interest and μ_0 is a known mean (e.g., a historical control).

In Chapter 7 of the textbook, we presented the following formulas for test statistics:

$$n \geq 30 \quad z = \frac{\overline{X} - \mu_0}{s/\sqrt{n}} \text{ (Find critical value in Table 1C)}$$

$$n < 30 \quad t = \frac{\overline{X} - \mu_0}{s/\sqrt{n}}$$

(Find critical value in Table 2, $df = n - 1$)

When performing the test of hypothesis by hand, we computed the sample size, the mean and standard deviation, and then the test statistic. We used Table 1C or Table 2 in the Appendix of the textbook to find the appropriate critical values of z or t and compared the test statistic to the critical value to draw a conclusion. Excel does not have a specific analysis tool for a one-sample test of means. However, Excel can be used to compute the test statistic and the *p*-value to draw a conclusion.

Example 7.1. In Example 7.1 in the textbook, we analyzed data on expenditures on health care and prescription drugs. We specifically analyzed whether there was significant evidence of a reduction in expenditures from the reported value of $3302

per year. To test the hypothesis, a sample of 100 Americans were selected and their expenditures on health care and prescription drugs in 2005 were summarized as follows: $\overline{X} = \$3190$ and $s = \$890$. We now run the test using Excel.

The hypotheses are:

$$H_0: \mu = 3302$$

$$H_1: \mu < 3302$$

$$\alpha = 0.05$$

Because the sample size is large ($n > 30$), the appropriate test statistic is $z = \frac{\overline{X} - \mu_0}{s/\sqrt{n}}$.

We use Excel to compute the test statistic and the *p*-value. The data are entered into an Excel worksheet, as shown in Figure 7-1. We now compute the test statistic, z, and place it in cell B8. The formula is "=(B3−B6)/(B4/SQRT(B2))". The *p*-value is computed with the NORMSDIST function. Because this is a lower-tailed test, we use "= 1−NORMSDIST(ABS(z))". The test statistic and *p*-value are shown in Figure 7-2.

We do not reject H_0 because, $p = 0.1041 > \alpha = 0.05$. We do not have significant evidence to show that there is a reduction in expenditures from the reported value of $3302 per year. (Recall that when this test was done by hand, we compared the test sta-

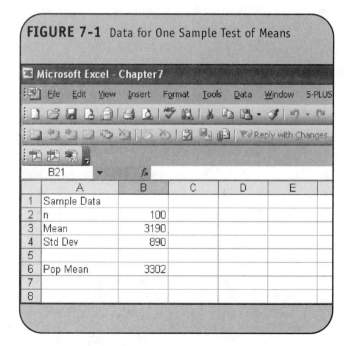

FIGURE 7-1 Data for One Sample Test of Means

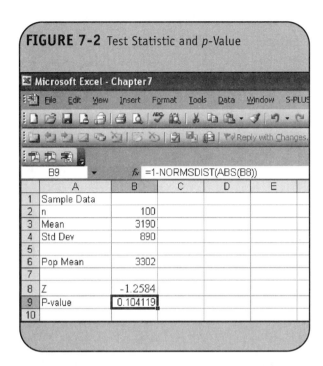

FIGURE 7-2 Test Statistic and *p*-Value

FIGURE 7-3 Data for One Sample Test of Means

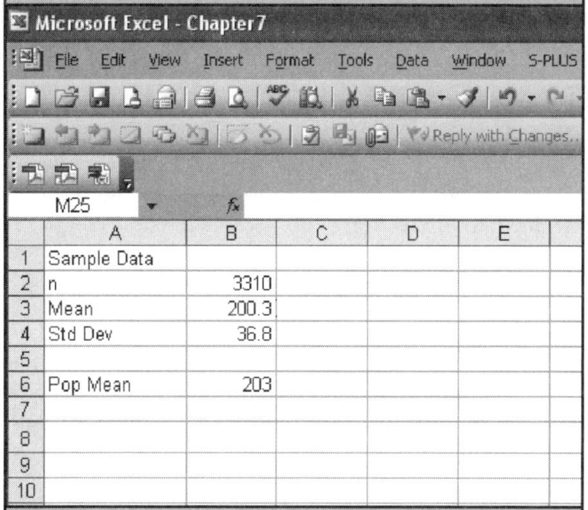

tistic $z = -1.26$ to the critical value from the standard normal distribution and did not reject H$_0$ because $-1.26 > 1.645$.)

Example 7.2. In Example 7.2 in the textbook, we tested whether the mean total cholesterol level in the Framingham Offspring Study was different from the national mean value of 203. The following statistics on total cholesterol levels of participants in the Framingham Offspring Study were available: $n = 3310$, $\overline{X} = 200.3$, and $s = 36.8$. Here we use Excel to test if there is statistical evidence of a difference in mean cholesterol level in the Framingham Offspring as compared to the national mean of 203.

The hypotheses are:

$$H_0: \mu = 203$$

$$H_1: \mu \neq 203$$

$$\alpha = 0.05.$$

Because the sample size is large ($n > 30$), the appropriate test statistic is $z = \dfrac{\overline{X} - \mu_0}{s/\sqrt{n}}$.

We use Excel to compute the test statistic and the *p*-value. The data are entered into an Excel worksheet, as shown in Figure 7-3. We now compute the test statistic, *z*, and place it in cell B8. The formula is "=(B3−B6)/(B4/SQRT(B2))". The two-sided *p*-value is computed with the NORMSDIST function

FIGURE 7-4 Test Statistic and *p*-Value

using "=2*(1−NORMSDIST(ABS(Z)))". The test statistic and *p*-value are shown in Figure 7-4.

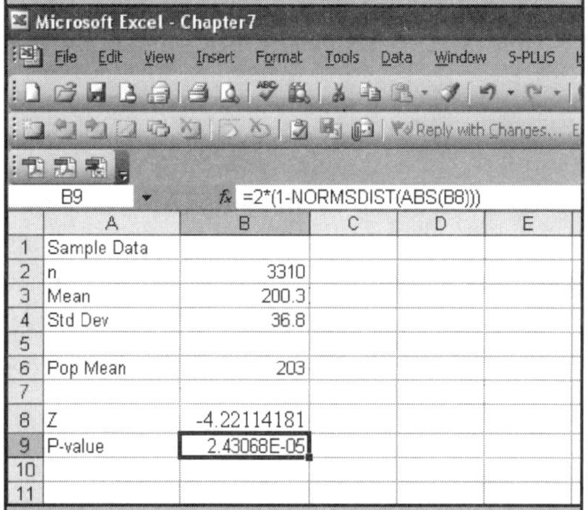

We reject H$_0$ because, $p = 0.00002 < \alpha = 0.05$. (Note that the *p*-value is given as $2.43E-05$, which is equivalent to $2.43 \times 10^{-5} = 0.0000243$.) We have significant evidence to show that the mean total cholesterol level in the Framingham

Offspring Study is different from the national value of 203. (Recall that when this test was done by hand, we compared the test statistic $z = -4.22$ to the critical value from the standard normal distribution and rejected H_0 because $-4.22 \leq -1.96$.)

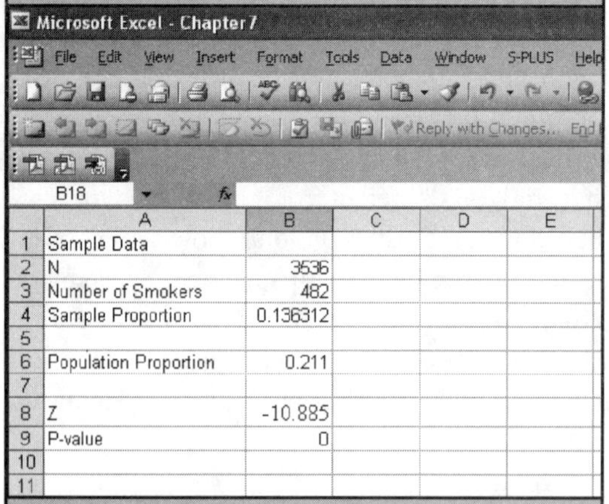

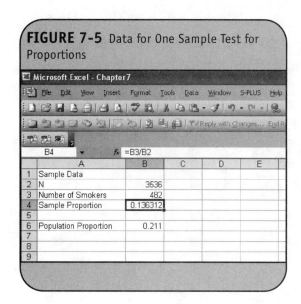

FIGURE 7-5 Data for One Sample Test for Proportions

	A	B	C	D	E
1	Sample Data				
2	N	3536			
3	Number of Smokers	482			
4	Sample Proportion	0.136312			
5					
6	Population Proportion	0.211			
7					
8					
9					

FIGURE 7-6 Test Statistic and *p*-Value

	A	B	C	D	E
1	Sample Data				
2	N	3536			
3	Number of Smokers	482			
4	Sample Proportion	0.136312			
5					
6	Population Proportion	0.211			
7					
8	Z	-10.885			
9	P-value	0			
10					
11					

7.2 TESTS WITH ONE SAMPLE, DICHOTOMOUS OUTCOME

For a one-sample test of hypothesis with a dichotomous outcome, the hypotheses are:

$$H_0: p = p_0$$

$$H_1: p > p_0 \quad H_1: p < p_0 \text{ or } H_1: p \neq p_0$$

where p is the proportion of successes in the population of interest and p_0 is a known proportion (e.g., a historical control).

In Chapter 7 of the textbook, we presented the following test statistic:

$$z = \frac{\hat{p} - p_0}{\sqrt{p_0(1-p_0)/n}} \quad \text{(Find critical value in Table 1C)}$$

When performing this test of hypothesis by hand, we computed the sample size, sample proportion, and then the test statistic. We used Table 1C in the Appendix of the textbook to find the appropriate critical value of z and compared the test statistic to the critical value to draw a conclusion. We now use Excel to conduct the test of hypothesis.

Example 7.3. In Example 7.4 in the textbook, we tested whether the prevalence of smoking in the Framingham Offspring Study was lower than the prevalence of smoking among American adults, reported as 21.1%. In the Framingham Offspring study, 482 of 3536 (13.6%) of the respondents were currently smoking at the time of the exam.

The hypotheses are:

$$H_0: p = 0.211$$

$$H_1: p < 0.211$$

$$\alpha = 0.05.$$

The appropriate test statistic is $z = \dfrac{\hat{p} - p_0}{\sqrt{p_0(1-p_0)/n}}$.

We use Excel to compute the test statistic and the p-value. The data are entered into an Excel worksheet, as shown in Figure 7-5. The sample proportion is shown in cell B4 and is computed by dividing the number of smokers in the sample by the sample size (i.e., B3 / B2).

We now compute the test statistic, z, and place it in cell B8. The formula is "=(B4−B6)/(SQRT(B6*(1−B6)/B2))". The one-sided p-value is computed with the NORMSDIST function using "=1−NORMSDIST(ABS(Z))". The test statistic and p-value are shown in Figure 7-6.

In this test, the test statistic is $z = -10.89$ and we reject H_0 because $p = 0 < \alpha = 0.05$. We have statistically significant evidence to show that the prevalence of smoking in the

Framingham Offspring is lower than the prevalence of smoking among American adults reported at 21.1%.

7.3   TESTS WITH ONE SAMPLE, DISCRETE OUTCOME: THE CHI-SQUARE GOODNESS-OF-FIT TEST

For an χ^2 goodness-of-fit test, the hypotheses are:

$$H_0: p_1 = p_{10}, p_2 = p_{20}, ..., p_k = p_{k0}$$

$$H_1: H_0 \text{ is false}$$

where p_i are the sample proportions of successes in each response category and p_{i0} are the known proportions in each response category.

In Chapter 7 of the textbook, we presented the following formula for the test statistic:

$$\chi^2 = \sum \frac{(O-E)^2}{E} \text{ (Find critical value in Table 3, } df = k - 1)$$

where O = observed frequency, E = expected frequency (i.e., sample data) in each of the response categories and k = the number of response options.

When performing the goodness-of-fit test by hand, we computed the expected frequencies for each category and then computed the test statistic. We then used Table 3 in the Appendix of the textbook to find the appropriate critical value from the χ^2 distribution and compared the test statistic to the critical value to draw a conclusion.

Excel does not have a specific analysis tool to perform the χ^2 goodness-of-fit test. However, it does have a CHIDIST function, which can be used to produce p-values. The CHIDIST function is used as "=CHIDIST(χ^2, df)". To use the CHIDIST function, we specify the test statistic, χ^2, and the degrees of freedom. For the χ^2 goodness-of-fit test, df = $k - 1$, where k represents the number of response categories. The CHIDIST function returns the area in the right tail of the distribution, which is the p-value for the χ^2 goodness-of-fit test. We now use Excel to conduct a goodness-of-fit test.

Example 7.4. In Example 7.6 of the textbook, we analyzed a university's survey of its graduates in which demographic and health information were collected for future planning purposes. In response to a question on regular exercise, 60% of all graduates reported getting no regular exercise, 25% reported exercising sporadically, and 15% reported exercising regularly as undergraduates. The next year, the university launched a health-promotion campaign on campus in an attempt to increase health behaviors among undergraduates and conducted another survey that was completed by 470 graduates. The data

TABLE 7-1 Data from University Survey

	No Regular Exercise	Sporadic Exercise	Regular Exercise	Total
Number of students	255	125	90	470

shown in Table 7-1 were collected. Based on the data, is there evidence of a shift in the distribution of responses to the exercise question following the implementation of the health-promotion campaign on campus?

The hypotheses are:

$$H_0: p_1 = 0.60, p_2 = 0.25, p_3 = 0.15, \text{ or equivalently}$$

$$H_0: \text{Distribution of responses is 0.60, 0.25, 0.15}$$

$$H_1: H_0 \text{ is false}$$

$$\alpha = 0.05$$

The appropriate test statistic is $\chi^2 = \sum \frac{(O-E)^2}{E}$.

Recall that the expected frequencies (E) are computed based on the assumption that H_0 is true. The data for the test are entered into an Excel worksheet, as shown in Figure 7-7. The sample data (i.e., the numbers of students in each response category) are the observed frequencies. The total sample size is computed using the SUM function and is shown in cell B6.

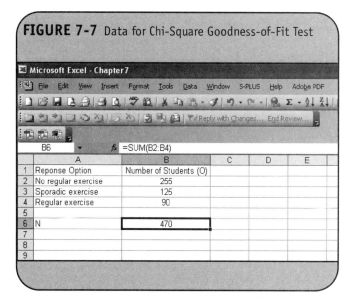

FIGURE 7-7 Data for Chi-Square Goodness-of-Fit Test

We compute the expected frequencies by multiplying the hypothesized or expected proportions in each response category (from H_0) by the total sample size. The expected proportions are first entered into the Excel worksheet in column C. We then multiply the expected proportions in column C by the sample size to produce the expected frequencies. For example, the expected frequency in cell D2 is computed using "=C2*\$B\$6". (Notice that we use the absolute cell address for the total sample size so that the same value is used to compute each expected frequency.) The expected proportions and expected frequencies are shown in Figure 7-8.

We now compute $(O - E)^2 / E$ in each response category and sum to produce the χ^2 statistic. The χ^2 test statistic is shown in cell E6. The p-value is computed with the CHIDIST function using "=CHIDIST(E6,2)", where "2" reflects the degrees of freedom ($df = k - 1 = 3 - 1 = 2$). The test statistic and p-value are shown in Figure 7-9.

In this test, the test statistic is $\chi^2 = 8.46$ and we reject H_0 because $p = 0.0146 < \alpha = 0.05$. We have statistically significant

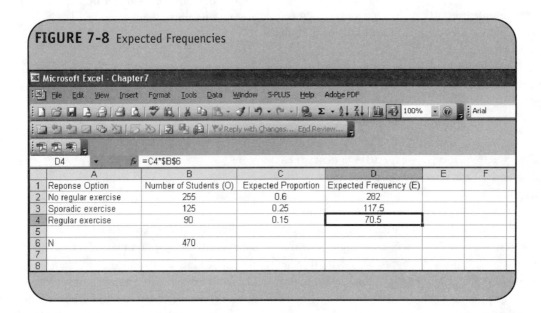

FIGURE 7-8 Expected Frequencies

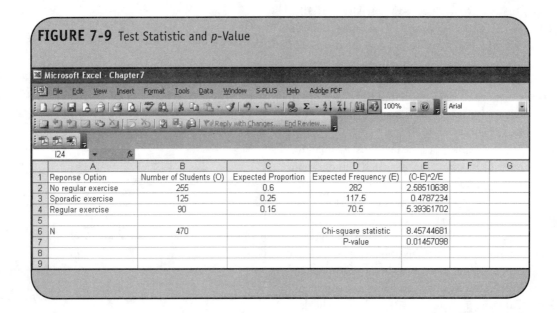

FIGURE 7-9 Test Statistic and p-Value

evidence to show that the distribution of responses is not 0.60, 0.25, 0.15.

7.4   TESTS WITH TWO INDEPENDENT SAMPLES, CONTINUOUS OUTCOME

For a two independent samples test of hypothesis with a continuous outcome, the hypotheses are:

$$H_0: \mu_1 = \mu_2$$

$$H_1: \mu_1 > \mu_2 \quad H_1: \mu_1 < \mu_2 \text{ or } H_1: \mu_1 \neq \mu_2$$

where μ_1 and μ_2 are the means of the two independent populations of interest.

In Chapter 7 of the textbook, we presented the following formulas for test statistics:

$$n_1 \geq 30 \text{ and } n_2 \geq 30 \quad z = \frac{\overline{X}_1 - \overline{X}_2}{S_p \sqrt{\frac{1}{n_1} + \frac{1}{n_2}}}$$

(Find critical value of z in Table 1C)

$$n_1 < 30 \text{ or } n_2 < 30 \quad t = \frac{\overline{X}_1 - \overline{X}_2}{S_p \sqrt{\frac{1}{n_1} + \frac{1}{n_2}}}$$

(Find critical value of t in Table 2, $df = n_1 + n_2 - 2$)

$$\text{where } S_p = \sqrt{\frac{(n_1-1)s_1^2 + (n_2-1)s_2^2}{n_1 + n_2 - 2}}$$

When performing tests of hypothesis by hand, we computed the sample sizes, means, and standard deviations in each sample. We then computed the pooled estimate of the common standard deviation, S_p, and the test statistic. We then used Table 1C or Table 2 in the Appendix of the textbook to find the appropriate critical values of z or t and compared the test statistic to the critical value to draw a conclusion. We now use Excel to conduct the test of hypothesis.

Example 7.5. A clinical trial is run to compare an experimental drug to a placebo for its effectiveness in lowering systolic blood pressure. A total of 18 participants are enrolled in the study and randomly assigned to receive either the experimental drug or placebo. After 6 weeks on the assigned treatment, each patient's systolic blood pressure is measured and the data are shown here:

Experimental drug 125 130 135 121 140 137 129 145 115

Placebo   145 140 132 129 145 150 160 140 120

Is there statistical evidence of a difference in mean systolic blood pressures between treatments? We now run the test using Excel.

The hypotheses are:

$$H_0: \mu_1 = \mu_2$$

$$H_1: \mu_1 \neq \mu_2 \qquad \alpha = 0.05$$

Because the sample sizes are small (both $n_1 < 30$ and $n_2 < 30$), the appropriate test statistic is $t = \frac{\overline{X}_1 - \overline{X}_2}{S_p \sqrt{\frac{1}{n_1} + \frac{1}{n_2}}}$. Excel has an analysis tool to perform a two independent samples test of means in its Data Analysis ToolPak. We first enter the data into an Excel worksheet, as shown in Figure 7-10.

Under the "Tools/Data Analysis" option, we choose the "*t* Test: Two Sample Assuming Equal Variances" analysis tool shown in Figure 7-11. Excel offers other options to perform a two independent samples test for the equality of means that do not assume that the variances are equal and thus would not involve S_p. In Chapter 7 of the textbook, we presented guidelines for using the formulas that assume equal variances. Once we click "OK," Excel presents the dialog box shown in Figure 7-12.

In the dialog box, we specify the range of the data for each group. The data for variable 1 (experimental drug) is in cell A1 through cell A10 and the data for variable 2 (placebo) is in cell B1 through cell B10. Because we included the first row (A1

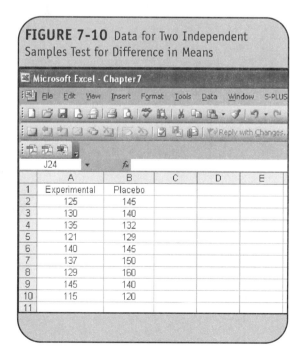

FIGURE 7-10 Data for Two Independent Samples Test for Difference in Means

	A	B	C	D	E
1	Experimental	Placebo			
2	125	145			
3	130	140			
4	135	132			
5	121	129			
6	140	145			
7	137	150			
8	129	160			
9	145	140			
10	115	120			
11					

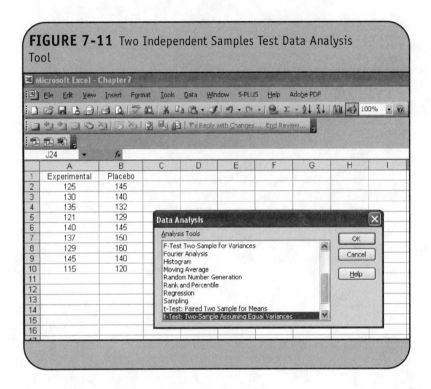

FIGURE 7-11 Two Independent Samples Test Data Analysis Tool

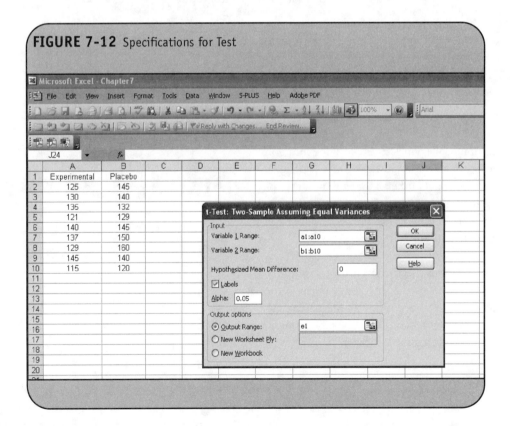

FIGURE 7-12 Specifications for Test

FIGURE 7-13 Results of Two Independent Samples Test for Difference in Means

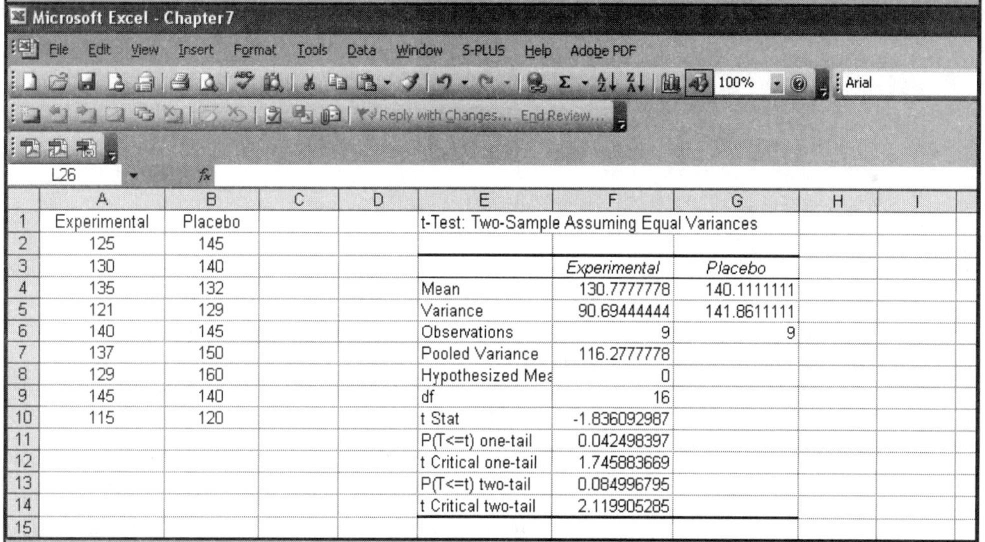

	A	B	C	D	E	F	G
1	Experimental	Placebo			t-Test: Two-Sample Assuming Equal Variances		
2	125	145					
3	130	140				*Experimental*	*Placebo*
4	135	132			Mean	130.7777778	140.1111111
5	121	129			Variance	90.69444444	141.8611111
6	140	145			Observations	9	9
7	137	150			Pooled Variance	116.2777778	
8	129	160			Hypothesized Mea	0	
9	145	140			df	16	
10	115	120			t Stat	-1.836092987	
11					P(T<=t) one-tail	0.042498397	
12					t Critical one-tail	1.745883669	
13					P(T<=t) two-tail	0.084996795	
14					t Critical two-tail	2.119905285	
15							

and B1), we click the "Labels" box. We then specify the difference in means under the null hypothesis. For most situations, the difference is zero. We then specify the level of significance, $\alpha = 0.05$, and specify a location for the results. In Figure 7-12, we request that Excel places the results in the current worksheet and we specify the top-left corner of the results table as E1. The results are shown in Figure 7-13.

The mean systolic blood pressure for patients on the experimental drug is 130.8 as compared to 140.1 for patients on the placebo. The estimate of the pooled variance is $S_p^2 = 116.3$, and the test statistic is $t = -1.84$. The two-sided p-value is 0.085, and thus we do not have significant evidence to show that there is a difference in mean blood pressures between treatments because $p = 0.085 > \alpha = 0.05$.

For two independent samples tests of means, as long as the variances are assumed to be equal, the "t Test: Two Sample Assuming Equal Variances" analysis tool can be used, regardless of the sample size. If the sample sizes (n_1 and n_2) are large, Excel makes the appropriate adjustments for larger samples (essentially, uses a z statistic) and produces an appropriate test statistic and p-value. The test statistic is always labeled t, even for large samples.

7.5 TESTS WITH MATCHED SAMPLES, CONTINUOUS OUTCOME

For a two dependent samples test of hypothesis with a continuous outcome, the hypotheses are:

$$H_0: \mu_d = 0$$

$$H_1: \mu_d > 0 \ H_1: \mu_d < 0 \text{ or } H_1: \mu_d \neq 0$$

where μ_d is the mean difference of the two dependent, matched or paired populations.

In Chapter 7 of the textbook, we presented the following formulas for test statistics:

$$n \geq 30 \quad z = \frac{\overline{X}_d - \mu_d}{s_d/\sqrt{n}} \quad \text{(Find critical value of } z \text{ in Table 1C)}$$

$$n < 30 \quad t = \frac{\overline{X}_d - \mu_d}{s_d/\sqrt{n}}$$

(Find critical value of t in Table 2, $df = n - 1$)

To perform the test of hypothesis by hand, we first computed difference scores, and then the sample size, mean, and standard deviation of the difference scores in the sample. We then computed the test statistic and the appropriate critical values of z or t from Table 1C or Table 2 in the Appendix of the text-

TABLE 7-2 Data from Cholesterol Study

Subject Identification Number	Baseline	6 Weeks
1	215	205
2	190	156
3	230	190
4	220	180
5	214	201
6	240	227
7	210	197
8	193	173
9	210	204
10	230	217
11	180	142
12	260	262
13	210	207
14	190	184
15	200	193

book and compared the test statistic to the critical value to draw a conclusion.

Excel has a procedure to perform a two dependent samples test of means in its Data Analysis ToolPak called the "*t* Test: Paired Two Sample for Means." We use this procedure to perform the test.

FIGURE 7-14 Data for Test of Mean Difference

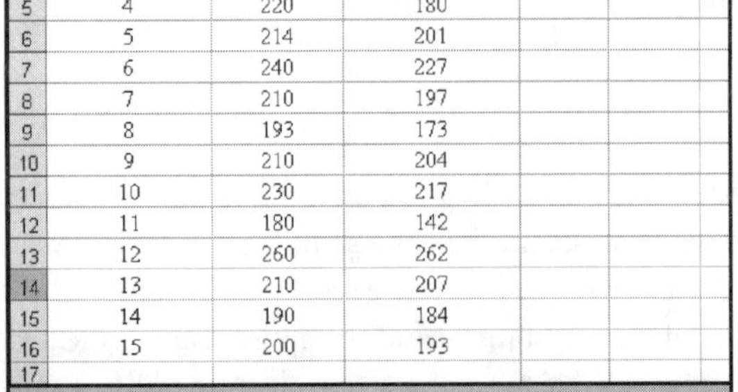

	A	B	C	D	E
1	ID	Baseline	6 Weeks		
2	1	215	205		
3	2	190	156		
4	3	230	190		
5	4	220	180		
6	5	214	201		
7	6	240	227		
8	7	210	197		
9	8	193	173		
10	9	210	204		
11	10	230	217		
12	11	180	142		
13	12	260	262		
14	13	210	207		
15	14	190	184		
16	15	200	193		
17					

Example 7.6. In Example 7.11 of the textbook, we evaluated the efficacy of a new drug for lowering cholesterol. Fifteen patients had a pre-treatment or baseline total cholesterol level measured, and then after taking the drug for 6 weeks, each patient's total cholesterol level was measured again. The data are shown in Table 7-2.

The hypotheses are:

$$H_0: \mu_d = 0$$

$$H_1: \mu_d > 0$$

$$\alpha = 0.05$$

Because the sample size is small, the appropriate test statistic is $t = \dfrac{\overline{X}_d - \mu_d}{s_d/\sqrt{n}}$.

We first enter the data into an Excel worksheet, as shown in Figure 7-14. Under the "Tools/Data Analysis" option, we choose the "*t* Test: Paired Two Sample For Means" analysis tool as shown in Figure 7-15. Once we click "OK," Excel presents the dialog box shown in Figure 7-16.

In the dialog box, we specify the range of the data for each measurement. The first measurement on each participant (variable 1) is the baseline measurement and it is in cell B1 through cell B16. The second measurement on each participant (variable 2) is the measurement taken at 6 weeks and it is in cell C1 through cell C16. Because we included the first row (B1 and C1), we click the "Labels" box. We then specify the difference in means under the null hypothesis. For most situations, the difference is zero. We then specify the level of significance, $\alpha = 0.05$, and specify a location for the results. In Figure 7-16, we specify the top-left corner of the results table as E1. The results are shown in Figure 7-17.

The mean cholesterol level at baseline is 212.8 and the mean cholesterol level at 6 weeks is 195.9. The two dependent samples test is based on difference scores (see Chapter 7 of the textbook for details). The test statistic is $t = 4.63$ and the one-sided p-value is 0.0002. We reject H_0 because $p = 0.0002 < \alpha = 0.05$. We have statistically significant evidence at $\alpha = 0.05$ to show that there is a reduction in cholesterol levels over 6 weeks. Notice that Excel does not produce summary statistics on the difference scores (i.e., $\overline{X}_d$, s_d). However, these values are used in the computation of the test statistic.

7.6 TESTS WITH TWO INDEPENDENT SAMPLES, DICHOTOMOUS OUTCOME

For a two independent samples test of a hypothesis with a dichotomous outcome, the hypotheses are:

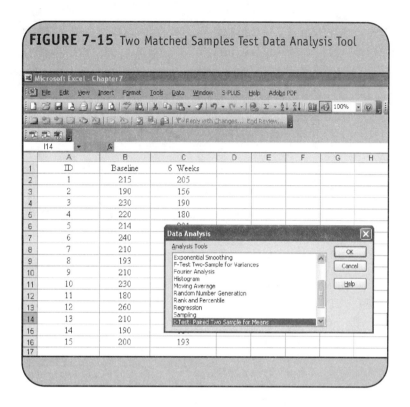

FIGURE 7-15 Two Matched Samples Test Data Analysis Tool

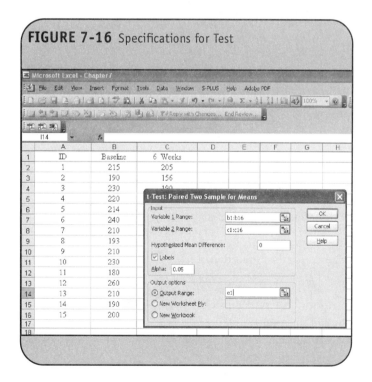

FIGURE 7-16 Specifications for Test

FIGURE 7-17 Results of Test for Mean Difference

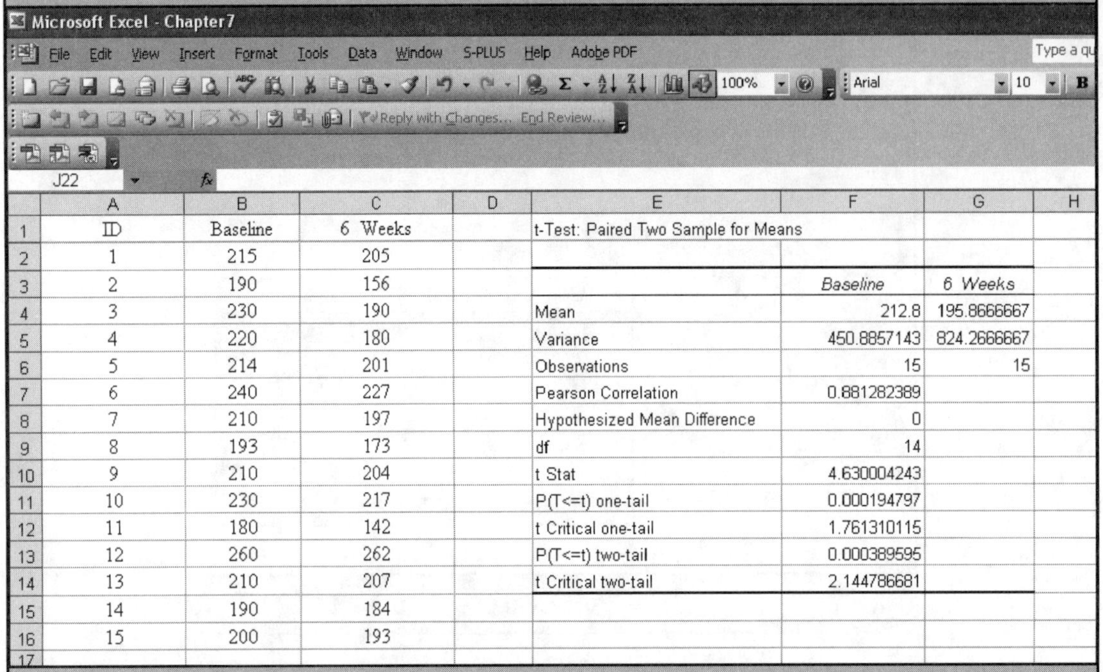

	A	B	C	D	E	F	G	H
1	ID	Baseline	6 Weeks		t-Test: Paired Two Sample for Means			
2	1	215	205					
3	2	190	156			Baseline	6 Weeks	
4	3	230	190		Mean	212.8	195.8666667	
5	4	220	180		Variance	450.8857143	824.2666667	
6	5	214	201		Observations	15	15	
7	6	240	227		Pearson Correlation	0.881282389		
8	7	210	197		Hypothesized Mean Difference	0		
9	8	193	173		df	14		
10	9	210	204		t Stat	4.630004243		
11	10	230	217		P(T<=t) one-tail	0.000194797		
12	11	180	142		t Critical one-tail	1.761310115		
13	12	260	262		P(T<=t) two-tail	0.000389595		
14	13	210	207		t Critical two-tail	2.144786681		
15	14	190	184					
16	15	200	193					
17								

$$H_0: p_1 = p_2$$

$$H_1: p_1 > p_2 \quad H_1: p_1 < p_2 \quad \text{or} \quad H_1: p_1 \neq p_2$$

where p_1 and p_2 are the proportions of successes in the two populations of interest.

In Chapter 7 of the textbook, we presented the following test statistic:

$$z = \frac{\hat{p}_1 - \hat{p}_2}{\sqrt{\hat{p}(1 - \hat{p})(1/n_1 + 1/n_2)}}.$$

(Find critical value of z in Table 1C)

where $\hat{p}_1$ is the proportion of successes in sample 1, $\hat{p}_2$ is the proportion of successes in sample 2, and $\hat{p}$ is the proportion of successes in the pooled sample, $\hat{p} = \dfrac{x_1 + x_2}{n_1 + n_2}$. Excel does not have a specific analysis tool to perform this test. We instead use Excel to compute the z statistic and the p-value.

Example 7.7. In Example 7.10 of the textbook, we analyzed data from a randomized trial designed to evaluate the effectiveness of a newly developed pain reliever as compared to a standard treatment in reducing pain in patients following joint replacement surgery. A total of 100 patients undergoing joint replacement surgery agreed to participate in the trial and were randomly assigned to receive either the new pain reliever

or the standard pain reliever following surgery, and were blind to the treatment assignment. Before receiving the assigned treatment, patients were asked to rate their pain on a scale of 0 to 10 with higher scores indicative of more pain. Each patient was then given the assigned treatment and after 30 minutes was again asked to rate their pain on the same scale. The primary outcome was a reduction in pain of 3 or more scale points (defined by clinicians as a clinically meaningful reduction). The data in Table 7-3 were observed in the trial.

We use Excel to test whether there is a statistically significant difference in the proportions of patients reporting a meaningful reduction (i.e., a reduction of 3 or more scale points). The hypotheses are:

TABLE 7-3 Data from Clinical Trial

Treatment Group	n	Reduction of 3 + Points Number	Proportion
New pain reliever	50	23	0.46
Standard pain reliever	50	11	0.22

$$H_0: p_1 = p_2$$

$$H_1: p_1 \neq p_2$$

$$\alpha = 0.05$$

The appropriate test statistic is $z = \dfrac{\hat{p}_1 - \hat{p}_2}{\sqrt{\hat{p}(1-\hat{p})(\frac{1}{n_1} + \frac{1}{n_2})}}$.

We now use Excel to compute the test statistic and the p-value. The data are entered into an Excel worksheet, as shown in Figure 7-18. The sample proportions are computed by di-

viding the numbers of successes (column C) by the sample sizes (column B) in each group.

Before computing the test statistic, z, we need to compute the overall proportion. This is placed in cell D5 and is computed as "=(C2+C3)/(B2+B3)". We next compute the test statistic, z, and place it in cell D7. The formula is "(D2−D3)/SQRT(D5*(1−D5)*(1/B2+1/B3))". The overall proportion and z statistic are shown in Figure 7-19. The last step involves computing the two-sided p-value using the NORMSDIST function as "=2*(1− NORMSDIST(ABS(Z)))". The p-value is shown in Figure 7-20.

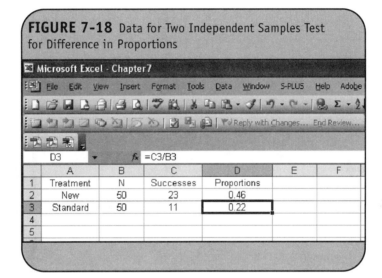

FIGURE 7-18 Data for Two Independent Samples Test for Difference in Proportions

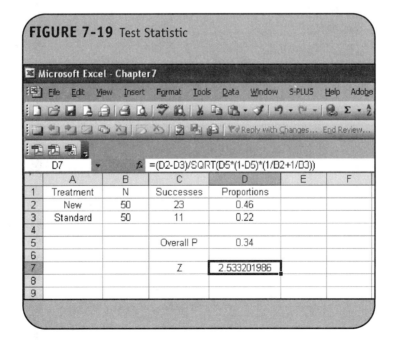

FIGURE 7-19 Test Statistic

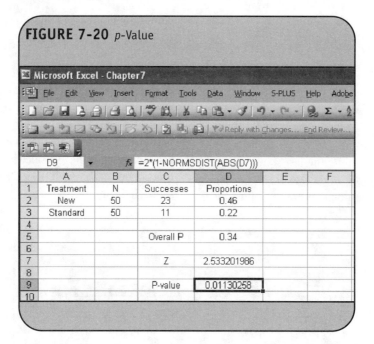

FIGURE 7-20 *p*-Value

In this test, the test statistic is $z = 2.53$ and we reject H_0 because $p = 0.011 \leq \alpha = 0.05$. We have statistically significant evidence at $\alpha = 0.05$ to show that there is a difference in the proportions of patients on the new pain reliever reporting a meaningful reduction (i.e., a reduction of 3 or more scale points) as compared to patients on the standard pain reliever.

7.7   TESTS WITH MORE THAN TWO INDEPENDENT SAMPLES, CONTINUOUS OUTCOME: ANALYSIS OF VARIANCE

In analysis of variance, the hypotheses are as follows:

$$H_0: \mu_1 = \mu_2 = \dots \mu_k$$

$$H_1: \text{Means are not all equal}$$

where μ_j is the mean in the jth group and k is the number of independent comparison groups.

In Chapter 7 of the textbook, we presented the test statistic for analysis of variance as:

$$F = \frac{\sum n_j (\overline{X}_j - \overline{X})^2/(k-1)}{\sum\sum(X - \overline{X}_j)^2/(N-k)}$$

(Find critical value in Table 4, $df_1 = k - 1$, $df_2 = N - k$)

TABLE 7-4 Data from Clinical Trial

Low-Calorie	Low-Fat	Low-Carbohydrate	Control
8	2	3	2
9	4	5	2
6	3	4	-1
7	5	2	0
3	1	3	3

where n_j is the sample size in the jth group, $\overline{X}_j$ is the sample mean in the jth group, and $\overline{X}$ is the overall mean. k represents the number of independent groups ($k > 2$) and N represents the total number of observations in the analysis.

Example 7.8. In Example 7.14 of the textbook, we analyzed data from a clinical trial comparing four weight-loss programs. The outcome of interest was weight loss, defined as the difference in weight at the start of the study (baseline) and weight at the end of the study (8 weeks), measured in pounds. A total of 20 patients agreed to participate in the study and were randomly assigned to one of the four diet groups. The data are shown in Table 7-4.

We will use Excel to conduct an ANOVA to test whether there is a statistically significant difference in the mean weight loss among the four diets. Excel has an analysis tool to perform

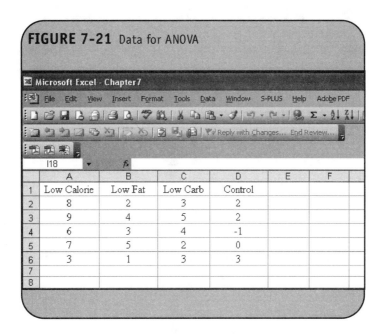

FIGURE 7-21 Data for ANOVA

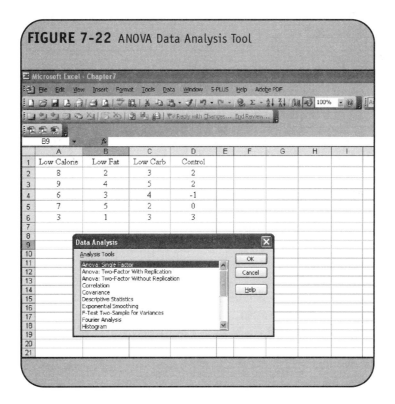

FIGURE 7-22 ANOVA Data Analysis Tool

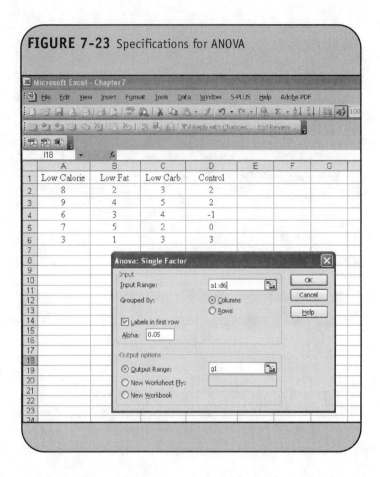

FIGURE 7-23 Specifications for ANOVA

an analysis of variance in its Data Analysis ToolPak. We first enter the data into an Excel worksheet, as shown in Figure 7-21. Under the "Tools/Data Analysis" option, we choose the "ANOVA: Single Factor" analysis tool shown in Figure 7-22. Once we click "OK," Excel presents the dialog box shown in Figure 7-23.

In the dialog box, we specify the range of the data. In this analysis tool, we specify the range of cells containing data on all groups. The data are in cell A1 through cell D6. Because we included the first row (A1 through D1), we click the "Labels" box. We then specify the level of significance, $\alpha = 0.05$, and a location for the results. In Figure 7-23, we request that Excel places the results in the current worksheet and we specify the top-left corner of the results table as G1. The results are shown in Figure 7-24.

Excel first provides summary statistics on each group. Specifically, Excel shows the count (n), sum (ΣX), average ($\overline{X}$), and variance (s^2) in each group. Excel then generates an ANOVA table similar to the one we produced in Chapter 7 of the textbook when conducting an ANOVA by hand. Excel provides sums of squares (SS), degrees of freedom (df), mean squares (MS = SS / df), and the test statistic, F. Excel also pro-

duces the p-value and the critical value of F for a test with a 5% level of significance. The p-value is 0.0013, and thus we reject H_0. We have statistically significant evidence at $\alpha = 0.05$ to show that there is a difference in mean weight loss among the four diets.

7.8 TESTS FOR TWO OR MORE INDEPENDENT SAMPLES, DISCRETE OUTCOME: THE CHI-SQUARE TEST OF INDEPENDENCE

For a test of independence, the hypotheses are:

H_0: The distribution of the outcome is independent of the groups

$$H_1: H_0 \text{ is false}$$

In Chapter 7 of the textbook, we presented for the test statistic:

$$\chi^2 = \sum \frac{(O-E)^2}{E}$$

[Find critical value in Table 3, $df = (r - 1)(c - 1)$]

FIGURE 7-24 Results of ANOVA

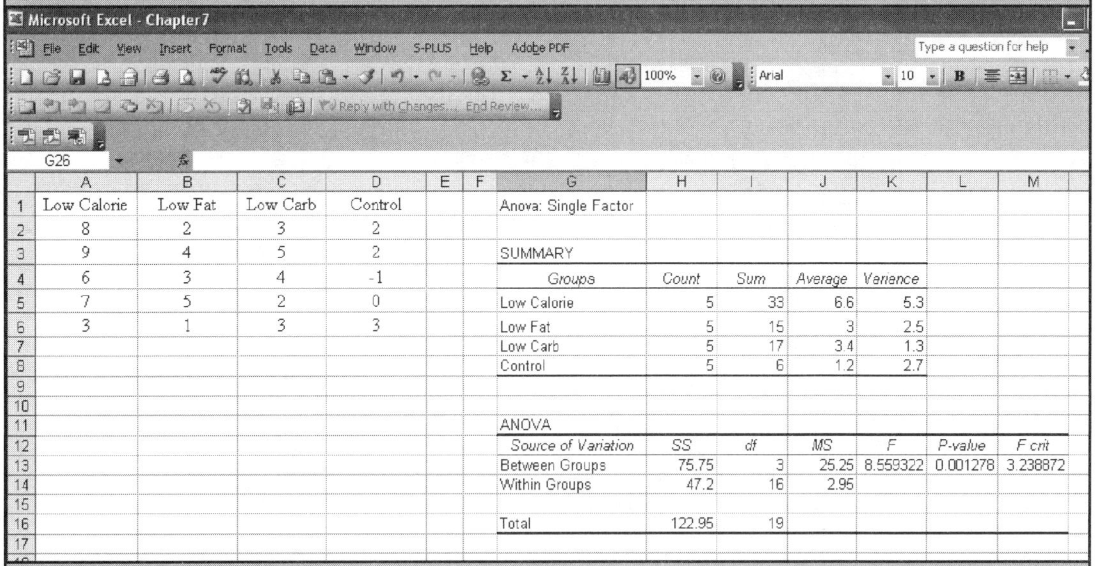

	A	B	C	D	E	F	G	H	I	J	K	L	M
1	Low Calorie	Low Fat	Low Carb	Control			Anova: Single Factor						
2	8	2	3	2									
3	9	4	5	2			SUMMARY						
4	6	3	4	-1			*Groups*	*Count*	*Sum*	*Average*	*Variance*		
5	7	5	2	0			Low Calorie	5	33	6.6	5.3		
6	3	1	3	3			Low Fat	5	15	3	2.5		
7							Low Carb	5	17	3.4	1.3		
8							Control	5	6	1.2	2.7		
9													
10													
11							ANOVA						
12							*Source of Variation*	*SS*	*df*	*MS*	*F*	*P-value*	*F crit*
13							Between Groups	75.75	3	25.25	8.559322	0.001278	3.238872
14							Within Groups	47.2	16	2.95			
15													
16							Total	122.95	19				
17													

where O = observed frequency (i.e., sample data), E=expected frequency in each of the cells of the table, r = the number of rows in the two-way table, and c = the number of columns in the two-way table (where r and c correspond to the number of comparison groups and the number of response options in the outcome).

When performing the test of independence by hand, we computed the expected frequencies for each category and then computed the test statistic. We then used Table 3 in the Appendix of the textbook to find the appropriate critical value from the χ^2 distribution and compared the test statistic to the critical value to draw a conclusion.

Excel does not have a specific analysis tool to perform the χ^2 test of independence. We will again use the CHIDIST function to produce p-values. We used this function for the χ^2 goodness-of-fit test as "=CHIDIST(χ^2, df)".

Again, to use the CHIDIST function we specify the test statistic, χ^2, and the degrees of freedom. For the χ^2 test of independence, df = $(r - 1) \times (c - 1)$. The CHIDIST function returns the area in the right tail of the distribution, which is the p-value for the χ^2 test of independence. We will now use Excel to conduct a test of independence.

Example 7.9. In Example 7.4 of the Excel workbook (and in Example 7.16 of the textbook), we examined data from a survey of university graduates that assessed, among other things, how frequently students exercised. Here we want to test whether there is a relationship between exercise and students' living arrangements. The data are shown in Table 7-5.

TABLE 7-5 Data from University Survey

	No Regular Exercise	Sporadic Exercise	Regular Exercise	Total
Dormitory	32	30	28	90
On-campus apartment	74	64	42	180
Off-campus apartment	110	25	15	150
At home	39	6	5	50
Total	255	125	90	470

The hypotheses are:

H_0: Living arrangement and exercise are independent

H_1: H_0 is false

$\alpha = 0.05$

The appropriate test statistic is $\chi^2 = \sum \frac{(O-E)^2}{E}$.

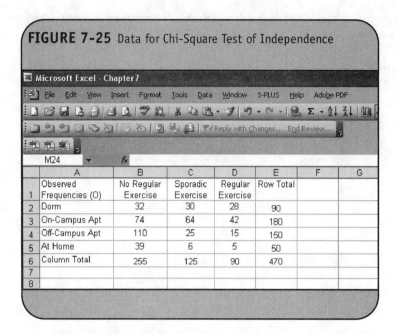

FIGURE 7-25 Data for Chi-Square Test of Independence

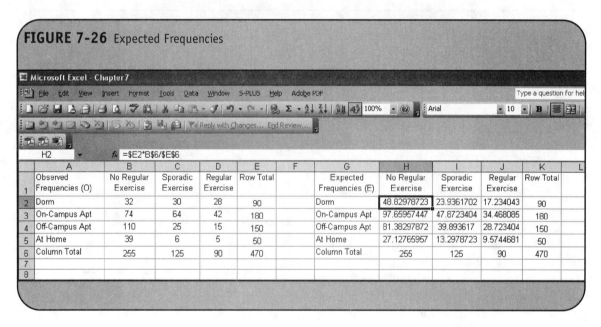

FIGURE 7-26 Expected Frequencies

Recall that the expected frequencies (E) are computed based on the assumption that H_0 is true. The data for the test are entered into an Excel worksheet, as shown in Figure 7-25. The sample data (i.e., the numbers of students in each cell of the table) are the observed frequencies in the table. The row and column totals are computed using the SUM function. For example, the column total in B6 is computed using "=SUM(B2:B5)". The row total in E2 is computed using "=SUM(B2:D2)". The grand total in E6 is computed by summing the column totals using "=SUM(B6:D6)".

This is equivalent to summing the row totals using "=SUM(E2:E5)".

We next compute the expected frequencies using the following:

$$\text{Expected cell frequency} = \frac{\text{Row total} \times \text{column total}}{N}$$

The expected frequencies are placed in another table, as shown in Figure 7-26.

To compute the expected frequencies, we need to use both relative and absolute cell addresses. For example, the expected frequency in cell H2 is computed using "=$E2*B$6/$E$6". The row total is referenced as $E2. We place a "$" in front of the column to freeze the column address on row totals that are contained in column E. We do the same for the column total, B$6, except we freeze the row address on row 6, which contains the column totals. The total sample size is in cell $E$6. When we copy the formula to cell H3, for example, the formula is updated to "=$E3*B$6/$E$6". The sums of the expected frequencies across rows and down columns are equal to the sums of the observed frequencies across rows and down columns.

We now compute $(O - E)^2 / E$ in each cell of the table. Once we compute these, we sum to produce the χ^2 statistic. The $(O - E)^2 / E$ values for each cell are shown in Figure 7-27. For example, in cell F9 the formula is "=(B2−H2)^2/H2". When we copy this formula to the other cells in the bottom table, the cell references are automatically updated (e.g., the formula in cell H12 is "=(D5−J5)^2/J5").

The χ^2 test statistic is computed by summing the $(O - E)^2 / E$ values in the nine cells. The test statistic is placed in cell G14 and is computed using "=SUM(F9:H12)". The p-value is computed with the CHIDIST function using "=CHIDIST (G14,6)", where "6" reflects the degrees of freedom, $df = (r - 1) \times (c - 1) = 3(2) = 6$. The test statistic and p-value are shown in Figure 7-28.

In this test, the test statistic is $\chi^2 = 60.44$ and the p-value is practically zero ($3.66 - 10^{-11}$). We reject H_0 because $p = 0 < \alpha = 0.05$. We have statistically significant evidence at $\alpha = 0.05$ to show that H_0 is false or that living arrangement and exercise are not independent (i.e., they are dependent or related).

7.9   PRACTICE PROBLEMS

1.   Data were collected in a clinical trial evaluating a new compound designed to improve wound healing in trauma patients. The new compound was compared against a placebo. After treatment for 5 days with the new compound or placebo, the extent of wound healing was measured and the data are shown in Table 7-6. Is there a difference in the extent of wound healing by treatment? (*Hint:* Are treatment and the percent wound healing independent?) Run the

FIGURE 7-27 Computing the Test Statistic

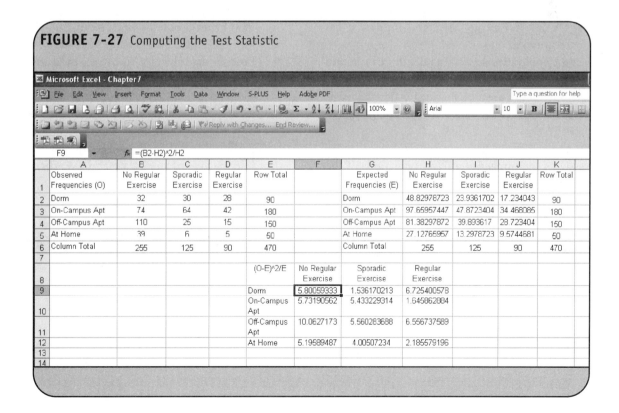

FIGURE 7-28 Test Statistic and *p*-Value

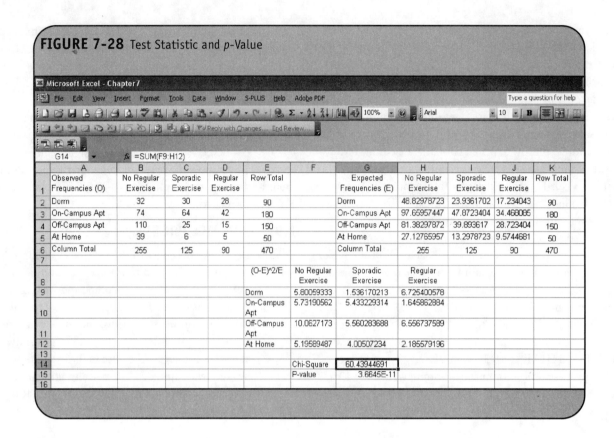

appropriate test at a 5% level of significance.

2. Use the data in Problem 1 and pool the data across the treatments into one sample of size $n = 250$. Use the pooled data to test whether the distribution of the percent wound healing is approximately normal. Specifically, use the following distribution: 30%, 40%, 20%, and 10% and $\alpha = 0.05$ to run the appropriate test.

3. Data were collected in an experiment designed to investigate the impact of different positions of the mother on fetal heart rate. Fetal heart rate is measured by ultrasound in beats per minute. The study included 20 women who were assigned to one position and had the fetal heart rate measured in that position. Each woman was between 28 weeks and 32 weeks gestation. The data are shown in Table 7-7. Is there a significant difference in mean fetal heart rates by position? Run the test at a 5% level of significance.

4. A clinical trial is conducted comparing a new pain reliever for arthritis to a placebo. Participants are

TABLE 7-6 Data for Practice Problems 1 and 2

Treatment	Percent Wound Healing			
	0–25	26–50	51–75	76–100
New compound ($n = 125$)	15	37	32	41
Placebo ($n = 125$)	36	45	34	10

TABLE 7-7 Data for Practice Problem 3

Back	Side	Sitting	Standing
20	21	24	26
24	23	25	25
26	25	27	28
21	24	28	29
19	16	24	25

TABLE 7-8 Data for Practice Problem 4

	Pain Relief	No Pain Relief
New medication	44	76
Placebo	21	99

randomly assigned to receive the new treatment or a placebo and the outcome is pain relief within 30 minutes. The data are shown in Table 7-8. Is there a significant difference in the proportions of patients reporting pain relief? Run the test at a 5% level of significance.

5. A clinical trial is planned to compare an experimental medication designed to lower blood pressure to a placebo. The objective of the study is to assess how systolic blood pressure changes over time untreated. Systolic blood pressures are measured at baseline and again 4 weeks later. Before starting the trial, a pilot study is conducted involving 7 partici-

pants. Is there a statistically significant difference in blood pressures over time? Run the test at a 5% level of significance.

Baseline: 120 145 130 160 152 143 126

4 Weeks: 122 142 135 158 155 140 130

6. A hypertension trial is mounted and 12 participants

TABLE 7-9 Data for Practice Problem 6

Placebo	New Treatment
134	114
143	117
148	121
142	124
150	122
160	128

Power and Sample Size Determination

In Chapter 8 in the textbook, we presented various formulas to determine the sample size for statistical inference. In applications where the goal is to generate a confidence interval estimate for an unknown parameter, the sample size is computed to ensure that the margin of error is sufficiently small. In applications where the goal is to perform a test of hypothesis, the sample size is computed to ensure that the test has a high probability of rejecting the null hypothesis when it is false (in other words, to ensure that the test has high power).

Excel does not have a specific analysis tool for determining sample size. However, we can use Excel's probability functions to implement the sample size formulas presented in Chapter 8.

8.1 SAMPLE SIZE ESTIMATES FOR CONFIDENCE INTERVALS WITH A CONTINUOUS OUTCOME IN ONE SAMPLE

In Chapter 8 of the textbook, we presented the following formula to estimate the sample size required to estimate the mean of a continuous outcome variable in a single population:

$$n - \left(\frac{z\sigma}{E}\right)^2$$

where z is the value from the standard normal distribution reflecting the confidence level that will be used (e.g., $z = 1.96$ for 95%), σ is the standard deviation of the outcome variable and E is the desired margin of error. The preceding formula generates the minimum number of subjects required to ensure that the margin of error in the confidence interval for μ does not exceed E.

To determine sample size requirements with Excel, we use the NORMSINV function to compute z values for confidence intervals as "=NORMSINV(*lower-tail area*)". To use this function for computing sample sizes, we specify the area under the curve in the lower tail of the standard normal distribution. For example, for a 95% confidence interval, the area in the lower tail is 0.975. Figure 8-1 shows the standard normal distribution, z, and the z values that hold the middle 95% of the distribution, $P(-1.96 \leq X \leq 1.96) = 0.95$.

To use the NORMSINV function for computing sample sizes, we specify the probability in the lower tail of the standard normal distribution for the desired confidence level. For example, if a 95% confidence interval is planned, we specify "=NORMSINV(0.975)", which returns 1.96. If a 90% confidence interval is planned, we specify "=NORMSINV(0.95)", which returns 1.645.

Example 8.1. In Example 8.1 of the textbook, we determined the sample size required to estimate the mean systolic blood pressure in children with congenital heart disease who were between the ages of 3 and 5 years old. The analysis was planned to estimate a 95% confidence interval and the investigator decided that a margin of error of 5 units was sufficiently precise. To determine the sample size, the standard deviation was assumed to be 20. The margin of error, standard deviation, and confidence level are input into Excel as shown in Figure 8-2. The z value is estimated using the NORMSINV function as shown in Figure 8-2.

Recall that the argument for the NORMSINV function is the area in the lower tail of the standard normal curve (Figure 8-1). If a 95% confidence interval is planned, the area in the lower tail is computed by first determining the total tail area as $(1 - 0.95)$ and then dividing this by 2 to determine the area in the upper tail. The lower-tail area is computed by

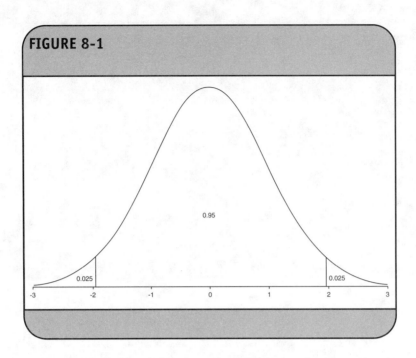

FIGURE 8-1

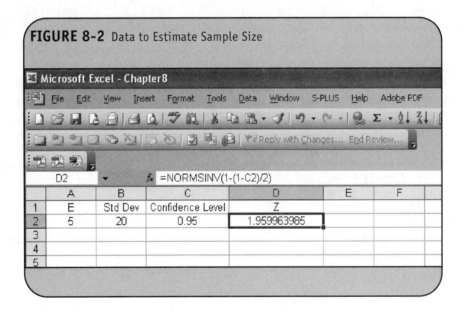

FIGURE 8-2 Data to Estimate Sample Size

subtracting the upper-tail area (i.e., $(1 - 0.95) / 2$) from 1. The argument for the NORMSINV function is "$(1-(1-C2)/2)$". This returns the value 1.96, which is the z value for a 95% confidence interval. The sample size is computed using the formula shown here. The result is in cell E2 and implemented using "$=(D2*B2/A2)^2$" and is shown in Figure 8-3.

Recall that the sample size formula always produces the minimum number of subjects required to ensure that the confidence interval has a margin of error not exceeding E. To determine the number of subjects required for the study, we must round up. This is done using Excel's ROUNDUP function. The ROUNDUP function is used as "$=ROUNDUP(num-ber\ to\ round,\ number\ of\ decimal\ places)$". For sample size computations, we round the value produced by the formula to the nearest integer (i.e., zero decimal places). The sample size required for the study is shown in Figure 8-4. To ensure that the

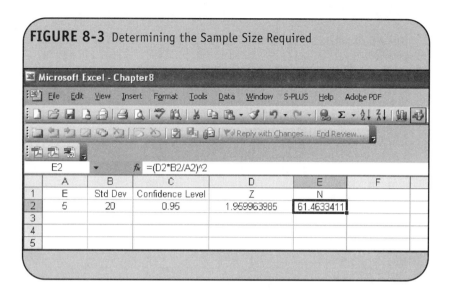

FIGURE 8-3 Determining the Sample Size Required

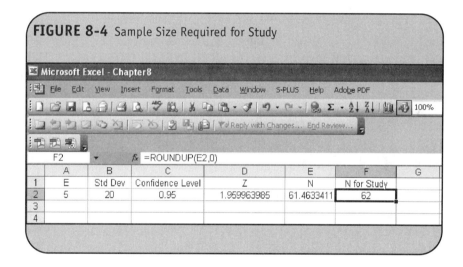

FIGURE 8-4 Sample Size Required for Study

95% confidence interval estimate of the mean systolic blood pressure in children between the ages of 3 and 5 years old with congenital heart disease is within 5 units of the true mean, a sample of size 62 is needed.

Once the Excel formulas are programmed, other scenarios can be considered. For example, suppose we wish to consider other margins of error (e.g., E = 5, 4, 3, 2) and other standard deviations (e.g., 20 and 15). The sample sizes for these other scenarios are determined by copying the formulas from cell D2 through cell F2 to cell D3 through cell F9. The sample sizes are shown in Figure 8-5.

If the standard deviation is 20, then to ensure that a 95% confidence interval estimate of the mean systolic blood pressure in children between the ages of 3 and 5 with congenital

heart disease is within 2 units of the true mean, a sample of size 385 is needed. If the standard deviation is 15, a sample of size 217 is needed. It is extremely important to accurately estimate the standard deviation, as it can dramatically affect the sample size.

8.2 SAMPLE SIZE ESTIMATES FOR CONFIDENCE INTERVALS WITH A DICHOTOMOUS OUTCOME IN ONE SAMPLE

In Chapter 8 of the textbook, we presented the following formula to estimate the proportion of successes in a dichotomous outcome variable in a single population:

$$n = p(1-p)\left(\frac{z}{E}\right)^2$$

FIGURE 8-5 Sample Size Estimates for Various Scenarios

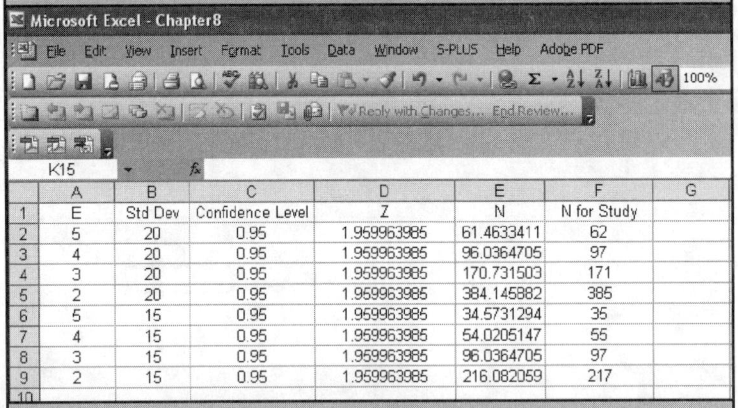

	A	B	C	D	E	F	G
1	E	Std Dev	Confidence Level	Z	N	N for Study	
2	5	20	0.95	1.959963985	61.4633411	62	
3	4	20	0.95	1.959963985	96.0364705	97	
4	3	20	0.95	1.959963985	170.731503	171	
5	2	20	0.95	1.959963985	384.145882	385	
6	5	15	0.95	1.959963985	34.5731294	35	
7	4	15	0.95	1.959963985	54.0205147	55	
8	3	15	0.95	1.959963985	96.0364705	97	
9	2	15	0.95	1.959963985	216.082059	217	

where z is the value from the standard normal distribution reflecting the confidence level that will be used (e.g., $z = 1.96$ for 95%), E is the desired margin of error and p is the proportion of successes in the population. If there is no information available to approximate p, then $p = 0.5$ can be used to generate the most conservative, or largest, sample size.

Example 8.2. In Example 8.3 of the textbook, we determined the sample size required to estimate the proportion of freshmen at a university who currently smoke (i.e., the prevalence of smoking). The investigator wanted to ensure that a 95% confidence interval estimate of the proportion of freshmen who smoke was within 5% of the true proportion. No information was available on the prevalence of smoking, thus $p = 0.5$ was used.

The margin of error, proportion ($p = 0.5$), and confidence level are input into Excel as shown in Figure 8-6. The z value is estimated using the NORMSINV function, as shown in Figure 8-6. Recall that the argument for the NORMSINV function is the area in the lower tail of the standard normal curve (Figure 8-1). The sample size is computed using the formula shown here. The result is in cell E2 and implemented using "=B2*(1−B2)*(D2/A2)^2" and shown in Figure 8-7.

The final step is to round up to the next integer using the ROUNDUP function. The sample size required for the study is shown in Figure 8-8. To ensure that a 95% confidence interval estimate of the proportion of freshmen who smoke is within 5% of the true proportion, a sample of size 385 is needed.

8.3 SAMPLE SIZE ESTIMATES FOR CONFIDENCE INTERVALS WITH A CONTINUOUS OUTCOME IN TWO INDEPENDENT SAMPLES

In Chapter 8 of the textbook, we presented the following formula to estimate the sample size required to estimate the difference in means in two independent populations:

$$n_i = 2\left(\frac{z\sigma}{E}\right)^2$$

where n_i is the sample size required in each group ($i = 1,2$), z is the value from the standard normal distribution reflecting the confidence level that will be used (e.g., $z = 1.96$ for 95%), and E is the desired margin of error. σ again reflects the standard deviation of the outcome variable. Recall from Chapter 6 in the textbook, when we generated a confidence interval estimate for the difference in means, we used S_p, the pooled estimate of the common standard deviation, as a measure of variability in the outcome (where S_p is computed as $Sp = \sqrt{\frac{(n_1-1)s_1^2 + (n_2-1)s_2^2}{n_1+n_2-2}}$. If data are available on variability of the outcome in each comparison group, then S_p can be computed and used in the sample size formula. However, it is more often the case that data on the variability of the outcome are available from only one group, often the untreated (e.g., placebo control) or unexposed group. This value can be used to determine the sample sizes.

Example 8.3. In Example 8.6 of the textbook, we determined the sample sizes required to compare two diet programs in obese children. The plan is to enroll children

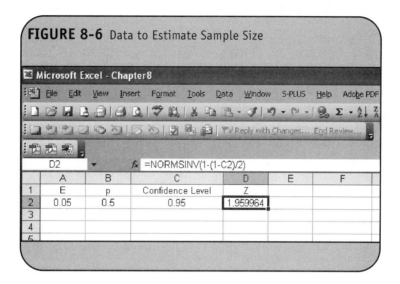

FIGURE 8-6 Data to Estimate Sample Size

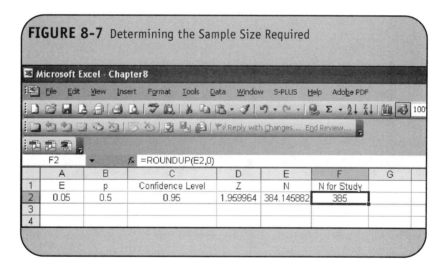

FIGURE 8-7 Determining the Sample Size Required

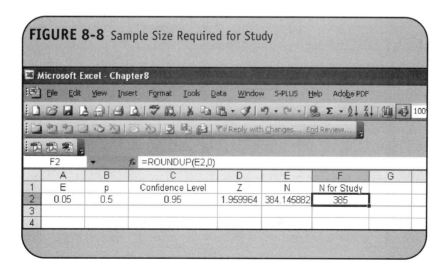

FIGURE 8-8 Sample Size Required for Study

and weigh them at the start of the study. Each child will then be randomly assigned to one of the competing diets (low-fat or low-carbohydrate) and followed for 8 weeks, at which time they will again be weighed. The number of pounds lost will be computed for each child. A 95% confidence interval will be estimated to quantify the difference in weight lost between the two diets, and the investigator would like the margin of error to be no more than 3 pounds. Based on adult studies, the common standard deviation was estimated at 8.1 pounds.

The margin of error, standard deviation, and confidence level are input into an Excel worksheet. The *z* value is estimated using the NORMSINV function as shown in Figure 8-9. The sample size required per group is computed using the formula shown here. The result is in cell E2 and implemented using "=2*(D2*B2/A2)^2" and shown in Figure 8-10. The final step is to round up to the next integer using the ROUNDUP function. The sample size required in each group for the study is shown in Figure 8-11.

Samples of size $n_1 = 57$ and $n_2 = 57$ will ensure that the 95% confidence interval for the difference in weight lost between diets will have a margin of error of no more than 3 pounds. (Note that in Chapter 8 of the textbook, we estimated the sample size at 56 per group because we carried only 2 decimal places in the by-hand computations. Excel carries more decimal places and therefore rounding up produces sample sizes of 57 per group.)

8.4 SAMPLE SIZE ESTIMATES FOR CONFIDENCE INTERVALS WITH A CONTINUOUS OUTCOME IN MATCHED SAMPLES

In Chapter 8 of the textbook, we presented the following formula to estimate the sample size required to estimate the mean difference of a continuous outcome variable in two matched populations:

$$n = \left(\frac{z\sigma_d}{E}\right)^2$$

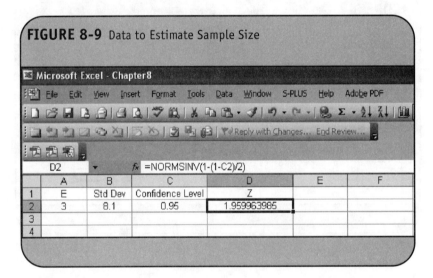

FIGURE 8-9 Data to Estimate Sample Size

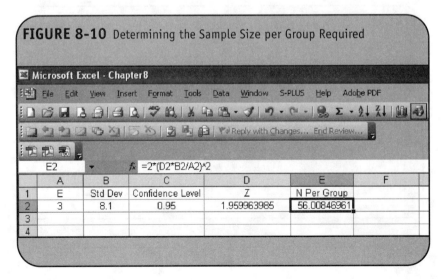

FIGURE 8-10 Determining the Sample Size per Group Required

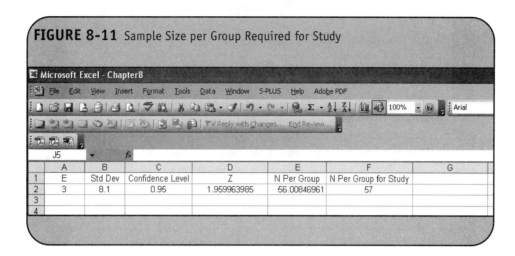

FIGURE 8-11 Sample Size per Group Required for Study

where z is the value from the standard normal distribution reflecting the confidence level that will be used (e.g., $z = 1.96$ for 95%), E is the desired margin of error, and σ_d is the standard deviation of the difference scores. It is extremely important that the standard deviation of the difference scores (e.g., the difference based on measurements over time or the difference between matched pairs) is used here to appropriately estimate the sample size.

Example 8.4. Consider again the diet study proposed in Example 8.3 of the Excel workbook (and in Example 8.7 in the textbook). The investigator considered an alternative design, a crossover trial, where each participant will follow each diet for 8 weeks. At the end of each 8-week period, the weight lost during that period will be measured. The difference in weight lost on the low-fat diet and the low-carbohydrate diet will be computed for each child and a confidence interval for the mean difference in weight lost will be computed. The investigator wanted to determine the sample size required to ensure that a 95% confidence interval estimate of the mean difference in weight lost between diets was within 3 units of the true mean difference.

The margin of error, standard deviation of the differences in weights, and the confidence level are input into an Excel worksheet. The z value is estimated using the NORMSINV function as shown in Figure 8-12. The sample size required is computed using the formula shown here. The result is in cell E2 and implemented using "=(D2*B2/A2)^2".

The final step is to round up to the next integer using the ROUNDUP function. The sample size required for the study is shown in cell F2 in Figure 8-13. To ensure that the 95% confidence interval estimate of the mean difference in weight lost between diets is within 3 units of the true mean, a sample of size 36 children is needed.

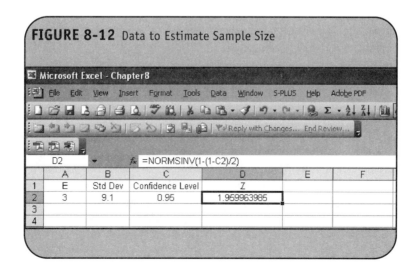

FIGURE 8-12 Data to Estimate Sample Size

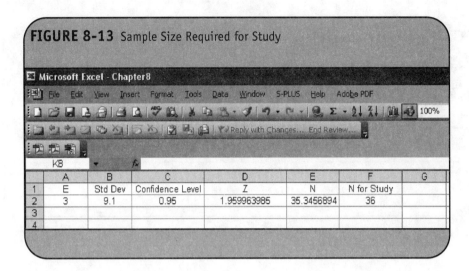

FIGURE 8-13 Sample Size Required for Study

8.5   SAMPLE SIZE ESTIMATES FOR CONFIDENCE INTERVALS WITH A DICHOTOMOUS OUTCOME IN TWO INDEPENDENT SAMPLES

In Chapter 8 of the textbook, we presented the following formula to estimate the difference in proportions between two independent populations (i.e., to estimate the risk difference):

$$n_i = \left[p_1(1-p_1) + p_2(1-p_2) \right] \left(\frac{z}{E} \right)^2$$

where n_i is the sample size required in each group ($i = 1,2$), z is the value from the standard normal distribution reflecting the confidence level that will be used (e.g., $z = 1.96$ for 95%), E is the desired margin of error, and p_1 and p_2 are the proportions of successes in each comparison group. Again, here we are planning a study to generate a 95% confidence interval for the difference in unknown proportions, and the formula to estimate the sample sizes needed requires p_1 and p_2. To estimate the sample size, we need approximate values of p_1 and p_2. The values of p_1 and p_2 that maximize the sample size are $p_1 = p_2 = 0.5$. Thus, if there is no information available to approximate p_1 and p_2, then 0.5 can be used to generate the most conservative, or largest, sample sizes.

Example 8.5. In Example 8.9 in the textbook, an investigator determined the sample size to estimate the impact of smoking on the incidence of prostate cancer. Men who are free of prostate cancer will be enrolled at age 50 and followed for 30 years. The plan is to enroll approximately equal numbers of smokers and nonsmokers in the study and to follow them prospectively for the outcome of interest, a diagnosis of prostate cancer. The plan is to generate a 95% confidence interval for the difference in proportions of smoking and nonsmoking men who develop prostate cancer. How many men should be enrolled in the study to ensure that the 95% confidence interval for the difference in proportions has a margin of error of no more than 5%? Estimates of the incidence of prostate cancer from a previous study were used to design the study: $p_1 = 0.34$ and $p_2 = 0.17$.

The margin of error, estimates of proportions, and the confidence level are input into an Excel worksheet. The z value is estimated using the NORMSINV function as shown in Figure 8-14. The sample size required per group is computed using the formula shown here. The result is in cell F2 and implemented using "$=(B2*(1-B2)+C2*(1-C2))*(E2/A2)\wedge 2$" and shown in Figure 8-15.

The final step is to round up to the next integer using the ROUNDUP function. The sample size required in each group for the study is shown in Figure 8-16. Samples of size $n_1 = 562$ men who smoke and $n_2 = 562$ men who do not smoke will ensure that the 95% confidence interval for the difference in incidence of prostate cancer will have a margin of error of no more than 5%.

8.6   ISSUES IN ESTIMATING SAMPLE SIZE FOR HYPOTHESIS TESTING

In Chapter 8 of the textbook, we presented formulas to determine the sample size required to ensure a specified power in a test of hypothesis. Excel does not have an analysis tool to perform the computations but the sample size formulas can be programmed into Excel to determine the appropriate sample sizes. The sample size formulas for hypothesis testing depend on the nature of the outcome variable (e.g., continuous or dichotomous) and also the number of comparison groups involved (e.g., one, two independent, or two matched).

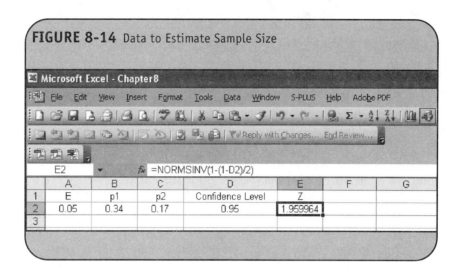

FIGURE 8-14 Data to Estimate Sample Size

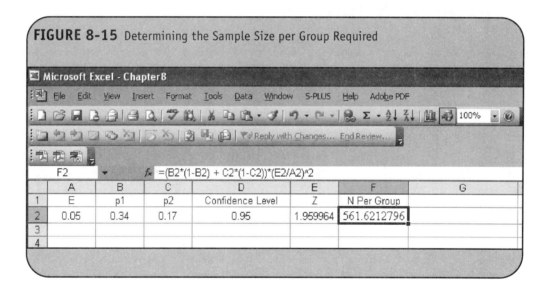

FIGURE 8-15 Determining the Sample Size per Group Required

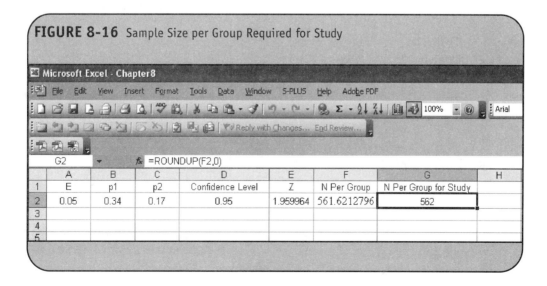

FIGURE 8-16 Sample Size per Group Required for Study

All of the sample size formulas contain the following two terms: $z_{1-\alpha/2}$ and $z_{1-\beta}$ where α is the probability of a Type I error or the specified level of significance (e.g., 0.05), β is the probability of a Type II error, and $1 - \beta$ is the specified power (e.g., 0.80, 0.90). $z_{1-\alpha/2}$ is the value from the standard normal distribution holding $1-\alpha/2$ below it and $z_{1-\beta}$ is the value from the standard normal distribution holding $1-\beta$ below it.

The NORMSINV function is used to compute these values. The NORMSINV function returns the value from the standard normal distribution, z, which holds a specified area below it (i.e., in the lower tail): "=NORMSINV(*lower-tail area*)". For example, if $\alpha = 0.05$, then $z_{1-\alpha/2} = z_{0.975}$ is computed by "=NORMSINV(0.975)". If power = 0.80, then $z_{0.80}$ is computed by "=NORMSINV(0.80)".

8.7   SAMPLE SIZE ESTIMATES FOR TESTS OF MEANS IN ONE SAMPLE

In Chapter 8 of the textbook, we presented a formula to determine the sample size required to ensure adequate power to test the following hypotheses about the mean of a continuous outcome variable in a single population:

$$H_0: \mu = \mu_0$$

$$H_1: \mu \neq \mu_0$$

where μ_0 is the known mean (e.g., a historical control). The formula for determining sample size to ensure that the test has a specified power is given below:

$$n = \left(\frac{z_{1-\alpha/2} + z_{1-\beta}}{ES}\right)^2$$

where α is the selected level of significance and $z_{1-\alpha/2}$ is the value from the standard normal distribution holding $1 - \alpha/2$ below it. $1 - \beta$ is the selected power and $z_{1-\beta}$ is the value from the standard normal distribution holding $1 - \beta$ below it. ES is the effect size, defined as follows:

$$ES = \frac{|\mu_1 - \mu_0|}{\sigma}$$

where μ_1 is the mean under the alternative hypothesis, μ_0 is the mean under the null hypothesis, and σ is the standard deviation of the outcome of interest.

Example 8.6. In Example 8.10 of the textbook, we determined the sample size required to test whether the mean blood glucose level in people who drink at least two cups of coffee per day is different from the reported mean of 95 mg/dl (the standard deviation was 9.8 mg/dl). Investigators wanted a sample size that would ensure 80% power to detect a mean of 100 mg/dl. A two-sided test is planned with a 5% level of significance.

Before we compute the sample size, we first must compute the effect size. This is done by entering the mean under the null, the mean under the alternative, and the standard deviation into an Excel worksheet, as shown in Figure 8-17.

The effect size is shown in cell B7 and is computed as "=ABS(B3−B1)/B5" where ABS is the Excel function to compute the absolute value of the difference in means under the null and alternative hypotheses. The next step is to compute the z value for the selected level of significance (i.e., $z_{1-\alpha/2}$) and the z value for the desired power (i.e., $z_{1-\beta}$). We first enter the level of significance, α, and the desired power. This is shown in Figure 8-18.

Recall that the argument for the NORMSINV function is the area in the lower tail of the standard normal curve (Figure 8-1). If a two-sided test is planned (which is generally the case for sample size planning) with a 5% level of significance, the area in the lower tail is defined as $(1 - \alpha/2)$. Thus, we specify "(1−B9/2)" as the argument to the NORMSINV function as shown in Figure 8-18. $z_{1-\beta}$ is determined in the same way using "=NORMSINV(B11)". The computations are shown in Figure 8-19. The next step is to compute the sample size based on the effect size and the appropriate z values for the selected α and power. This is shown in Figure 8-20.

FIGURE 8-17 Data to Estimate Sample Size

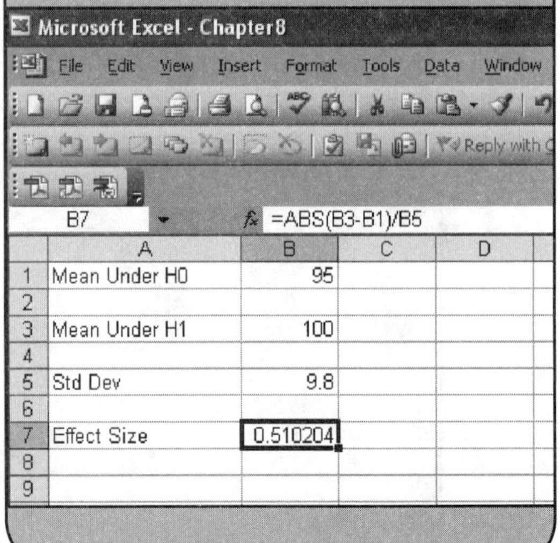

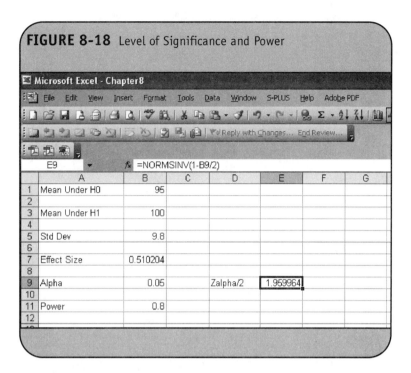

FIGURE 8-18 Level of Significance and Power

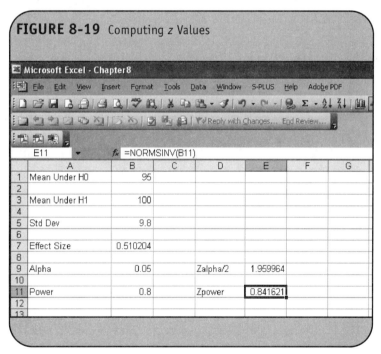

FIGURE 8-19 Computing z Values

Because the sample size formula always produces the minimum number of subjects required to ensure that the test has the specified power to detect the desired effect size at the specified level of significance, to determine the number of subjects required for the study, we must round up. This is done using Excel's ROUNDUP function. The sample size required for the study is shown in Figure 8-21. A sample of size $n = 31$ will ensure that a two-sided test with $\alpha = 0.05$ has 80% power to detect a 5 mg/dl difference in mean fasting blood glucose levels.

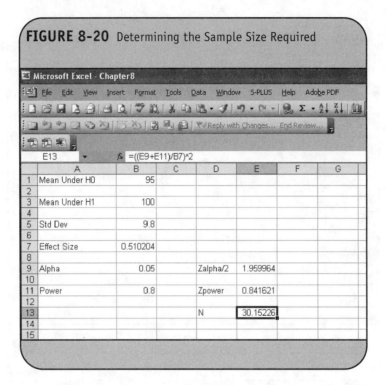

FIGURE 8-20 Determining the Sample Size Required

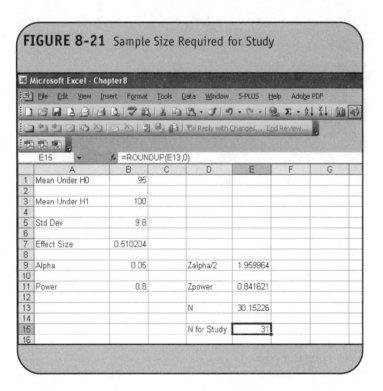

FIGURE 8-21 Sample Size Required for Study

8.8 SAMPLE SIZE ESTIMATES FOR TESTS OF PROPORTIONS IN ONE SAMPLE

In Chapter 8 of the textbook, we presented a formula to determine the sample size required to ensure adequate power to test the following hypotheses about the proportion of successes in a dichotomous outcome variable in a single population:

$$H_0: p = p_0$$

$$H_1: p \neq p_0$$

where p_0 is the known proportion (e.g., a historical control). The formula for determining sample size to ensure that the test has a specified power is given below:

$$n = \left(\frac{z_{1-\alpha/2} + z_{1-\beta}}{ES} \right)^2$$

where α is the selected level of significance and $z_{1-\alpha/2}$ is the value from the standard normal distribution holding $1-\alpha/2$ below it. $1-\beta$ is the selected power and $z_{1-\beta}$ is the value from the standard normal distribution holding $1-\beta$ below it. ES is the effect size, defined as:

$$ES = \frac{|p_1 - p_0|}{\sqrt{p_0(1-p_0)}}$$

where p_0 is the proportion of successes under H_0 and p_1 is the proportion of successes under H_1. The numerator of the effect size, the absolute value of the difference in proportions $|p_1 - p_0|$, again represents what is considered a clinically meaningful or practically important difference in proportions.

FIGURE 8-22 Data to Estimate Sample Size

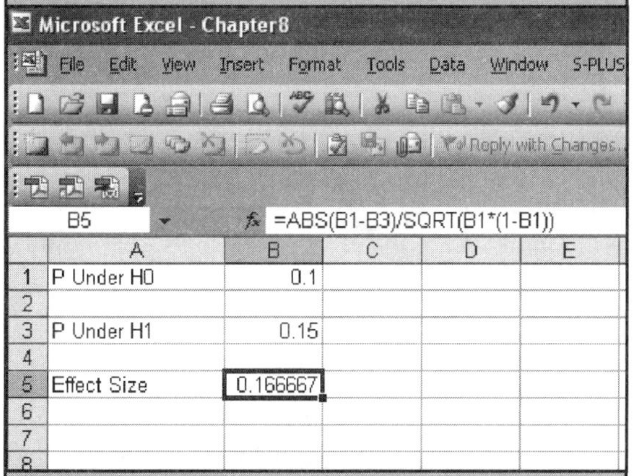

Example 8.7. In Example 8.13 in the textbook, we determined the sample size required to test whether the proportion of defective stents produced by a manufacturer was more than 10%. The manufacturer wanted the test to have 90% power to detect an absolute difference in proportions of 5% (i.e., from 10% to 15% defectives). How many stents must be evaluated? A two-sided test will be used with a 5% level of significance.

Before we compute the sample size, we first must compute the effect size. This is done by entering the proportion under the null and the proportion under the alternative into an Excel worksheet, as shown in Figure 8-22.

The effect size is shown in cell B5 and is computed as "=ABS(B3−B1)/SQRT(B1*(1−B1))", where ABS is the Excel function to compute the absolute value of the difference in proportions under the null and alternative hypotheses. The next step is to compute the z value for the selected level of significance (i.e., $z_{1-\alpha/2}$) and the z value for the desired power (i.e., $z_{1-\beta}$). We first enter the level of significance, α, and the desired power. We then use the NORMSINV function twice to compute $z_{1-\alpha/2}$ and $z_{1-\beta}$. This is shown in Figure 8-23.

The next step is to compute the sample size based on the effect size and the appropriate z values for the selected α and power. This is shown in Figure 8-24. As the final step, we round up to the next integer using the ROUNDUP function. The sample size for the study is shown in Figure 8-25.

A sample of size $n = 379$ stents will ensure that a two-sided test with $\alpha = 0.05$ has 90% power to detect a 5% difference in the proportion of defective stents produced. (When we computed the sample size by hand in the textbook, we determined that $n = 364$ stents were needed. The difference is because Excel is carrying more decimal places in the computations.)

8.9 SAMPLE SIZE ESTIMATES FOR TESTS OF DIFFERENCES IN MEANS IN TWO INDEPENDENT SAMPLES

In Chapter 8 of the textbook, we presented a formula to determine the sample size required to ensure adequate power to test the following hypotheses about the difference in means in two independent populations:

$$H_0: \mu_1 = \mu_2$$

$$H_1: \mu_1 \neq \mu_2$$

where μ_1 and μ_2 are the means in the two comparison populations. The formula for determining sample size required in each group to ensure that the test has a specified power follows:

$$n_i = 2 \left(\frac{z_{1-\alpha/2} + z_{1-\beta}}{ES} \right)^2$$

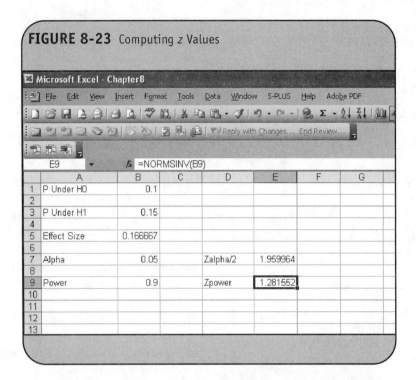

FIGURE 8-23 Computing z Values

FIGURE 8-24 Determining the Sample Size Required

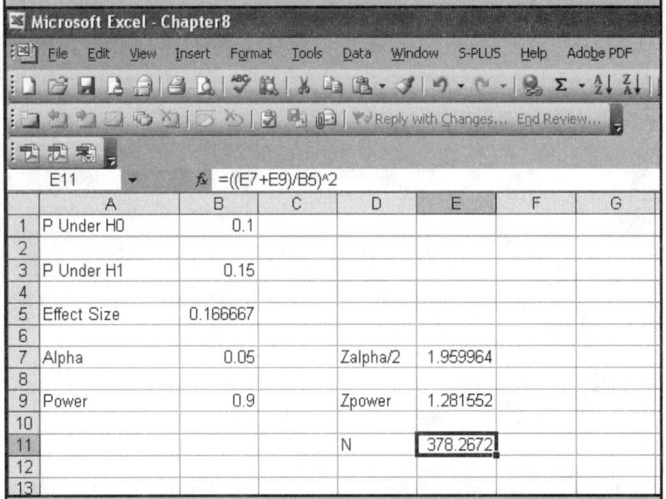

where n_i is the sample size required in each group ($i = 1,2$), α is the selected level of significance, and $z_{1-\alpha/2}$ is the value from the standard normal distribution holding $1 - \alpha/2$ below it, $1 - \beta$ is the selected power, and $z_{1-\beta}$ is the value from the standard normal distribution holding $1 - \beta$ below it. ES is the effect size, defined as:

$$ES = \frac{|\mu_1 - \mu_2|}{\sigma}$$

where $|\mu_1 - \mu_2|$ is the absolute value of the difference in means between the two groups representing what is considered a clinically meaningful or practically important difference in means. σ is the standard deviation of the outcome of interest. If data

FIGURE 8-25 Sample Size Required for Study

	A	B	C	D	E	F	G
1	P Under H0	0.1					
2							
3	P Under H1	0.15					
4							
5	Effect Size	0.166667					
6							
7	Alpha	0.05		Zalpha/2	1.959964		
8							
9	Power	0.9		Zpower	1.281552		
10							
11				N	378.2672		
12							
13				N for Study	379		
14							
15							

E13 = ROUNDUP(E11,0)

are available on variability of the outcome in each comparison group, then S_p (the pooled estimate of the common standard deviation) can be computed and used to generate the sample sizes. However, it is more often the case that data on the variability of the outcome are available from only one group, usually the untreated (e.g., placebo control) or unexposed group.

Example 8.8. In Example 8.14 in the textbook, we determined the sample sizes required for a clinical trial to evaluate the efficacy of a new drug designed to reduce systolic blood pressure. The plan was to enroll participants and to randomly assign them to receive either the new drug or a placebo and to measure systolic blood pressure in each participant after 12 weeks on the assigned treatment. Investigators indicated that a 5-unit difference in mean systolic blood pressure would represent a clinically meaningful difference. How many patients should be enrolled in the trial to ensure that the power of the test is 80% to detect this difference? A two-sided test is planned with a 5% level of significance and the standard deviation is assumed to be 19.0, based on data from the Framingham Heart Study.

We first compute the effect size based on the hypothesized difference in means under the alternative hypothesis and the standard deviation. The data are entered into an Excel worksheet as shown in Figure 8-26. The effect size is shown in cell B5 and is computed as "=ABS(B1)/B3". Notice that the hypothesized difference in means is specified in Figure 8-26. In

FIGURE 8-26 Data to Estimate Sample Size

	A	B	C	D
1	Difference in Means	5		
2				
3	Std Dev	19		
4				
5	Effect Size	0.263158		
6				
7				

B5 = ABS(B1)/B3

some applications, the means under the null and alternative are specified, in which case the difference is computed and used as the numerator in the computation of the effect size. We next enter the level of significance, α, and the desired power to compute $z_{1-\alpha/2}$ and the $z_{1-\beta}$. This is shown in Figure 8-27. The next step is to compute the sample size per group based on the effect size and the appropriate z values for the selected α and power. This is shown in Figure 8-28.

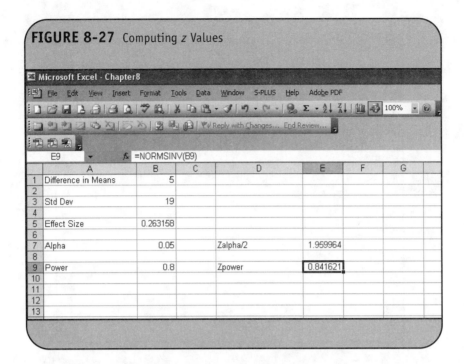

FIGURE 8-27 Computing *z* Values

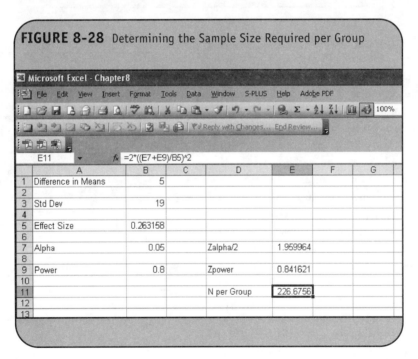

FIGURE 8-28 Determining the Sample Size Required per Group

Finally, because the sample size formula always produces the minimum number of subjects per group required to ensure that the test has the specified power to detect the desired effect size at the specified level of significance, to determine the numbers of subjects per group required for the study, we must round up. This is done using Excel's ROUNDUP function. The sample sizes required per group are shown in Figure 8-29.

Samples of size $n_1 = 227$ and $n_2 = 227$ will ensure that the test of hypothesis will have 80% power to detect a 5-unit difference in mean systolic blood pressures in patients receiving the new drug as compared to patients receiving the placebo.

FIGURE 8-29 Sample Size Required per Group for Study

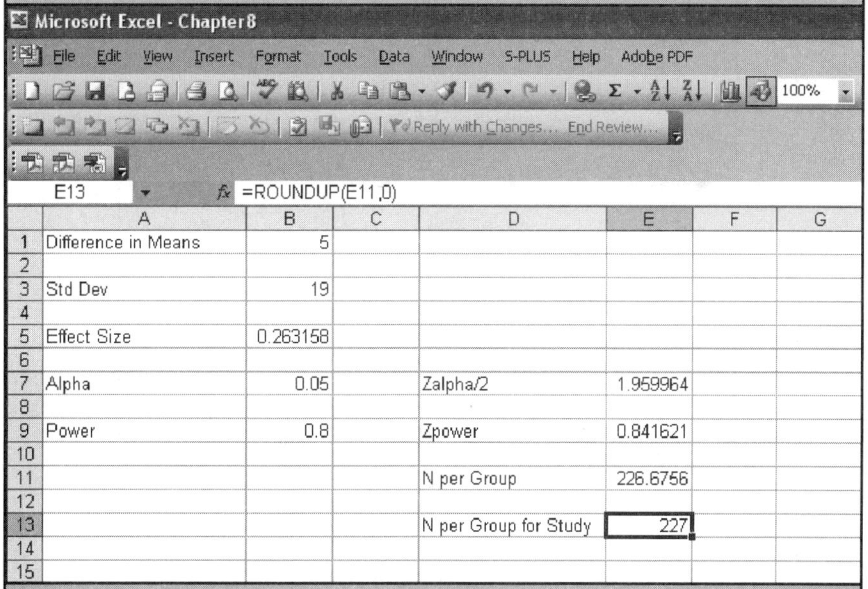

Microsoft Excel - Chapter8

E13 =ROUNDUP(E11,0)

	A	B	C	D	E	F	G
1	Difference in Means	5					
2							
3	Std Dev	19					
4							
5	Effect Size	0.263158					
6							
7	Alpha	0.05		Zalpha/2	1.959964		
8							
9	Power	0.8		Zpower	0.841621		
10							
11				N per Group	226.6756		
12							
13				N per Group for Study	227		
14							
15							

8.10 SAMPLE SIZE ESTIMATES FOR TESTS OF MEAN DIFFERENCES IN MATCHED SAMPLES

In Chapter 8 of the textbook, we presented a formula to determine the sample size required to ensure adequate power to test the following hypotheses about the mean difference in a continuous outcome based on matched populations:

$$H_0: \mu_d = 0$$

$$H_1: \mu_d \neq 0$$

where μ_d is the mean difference in the population. The formula for determining the sample size (i.e., number of participants, each of whom will be measured twice) required to ensure that the test has a specified power is:

$$n = \left(\frac{z_{1-\alpha/2} + z_{1-\beta}}{\text{ES}}\right)^2$$

where α is the selected level of significance and $z_{1-\alpha/2}$ is the value from the standard normal distribution holding $1-\alpha/2$ below it, and $1-\beta$ is the selected power, and $z_{1-\beta}$ is the value from the standard normal distribution holding $1-\beta$ below it. ES is the effect size, defined as:

$$\text{ES} = \frac{\mu_d}{\sigma_d}$$

where μ_d is the mean difference expected under the alternative hypothesis, H_1, and σ_d is the standard deviation of the difference in the outcome (e.g., the difference based on measurements over time or the difference between matched pairs).

Example 8.9. In Example 8.15 of the textbook, we generated sample size requirements for a crossover trial to compare two diet programs for their effectiveness in promoting weight loss. The proposed study will have each child follow each diet for 8 weeks and at the end of each 8-week period, the weight lost during that period will be measured. The difference in weight lost between the diets will be computed for each child and the plan is to test if there is a statistically significant difference in weight loss between the diets. How many children are required to ensure that a two-sided test with a 5% level of significance has 80% power to detect a mean difference of 3 pounds in weight lost between the two diets? Based on a previous study, the standard deviation in the differences in weight loss is estimated at 9.1 pounds.

We first compute the effect size based on the hypothesized mean difference between weight-loss programs and the standard deviation of the differences in weight loss. The data are entered into an Excel worksheet as shown in Figure 8-30.

The effect size is shown in cell B5 and is computed as "=B1/B3". We next enter the level of significance, α, and the

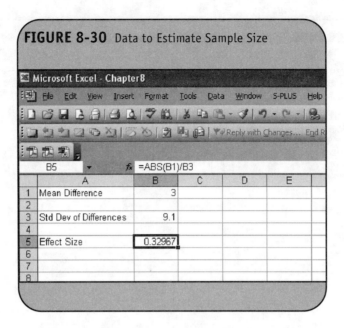

FIGURE 8-30 Data to Estimate Sample Size

FIGURE 8-31 Computing *z* Values

desired power to compute $z_{1-\alpha/2}$ and the $z_{1-\beta}$. This is shown in Figure 8-31. The next step is to compute the sample size based on the effect size and the appropriate *z* values for the selected α and power. This is shown in Figure 8-32.

Finally, because the sample size formula always produces the minimum number of subjects required to ensure that the test has the specified power to detect the desired effect size at the specified level of significance, to determine

the numbers of subjects required for the study, we must round up. This is done using Excel's ROUNDUP function. The sample sizes required per group are shown in Figure 8-33.

A sample of size $n = 73$ children will ensure that a two-sided test with $\alpha = 0.05$ has 80% power to detect a mean difference of 3 pounds between diets using a crossover trial (i.e., each child will be measured on each diet).

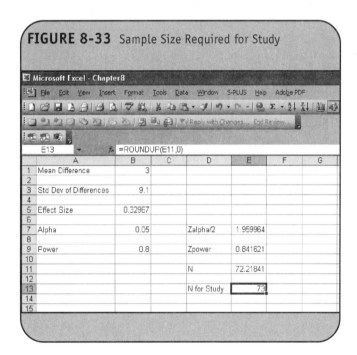

FIGURE 8-32 Determining the Sample Size Required

	A	B	C	D	E	F	G
1	Mean Difference	3					
2							
3	Std Dev of Differences	9.1					
4							
5	Effect Size	0.32967					
6							
7	Alpha	0.05		Zalpha/2	1.959964		
8							
9	Power	0.8		Zpower	0.841621		
10							
11				N	72.21841		
12							

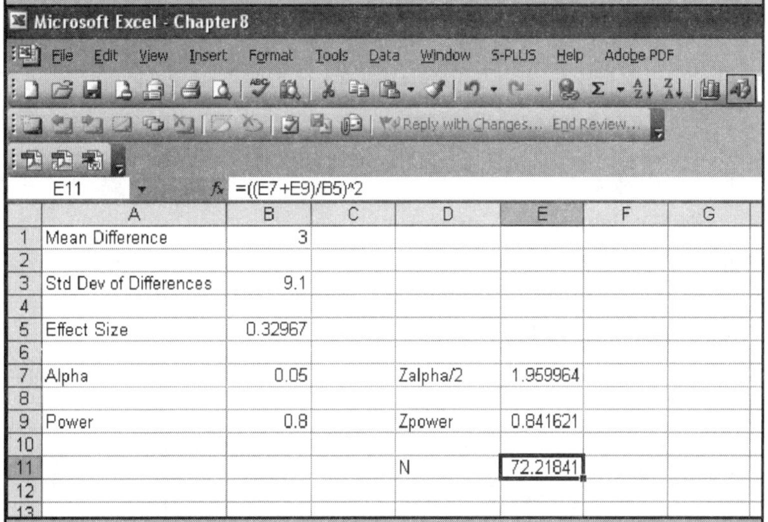

FIGURE 8-33 Sample Size Required for Study

	A	B	C	D	E	F	G
1	Mean Difference	3					
2							
3	Std Dev of Differences	9.1					
4							
5	Effect Size	0.32967					
6							
7	Alpha	0.05		Zalpha/2	1.959964		
8							
9	Power	0.8		Zpower	0.841621		
10							
11				N	72.21841		
12							
13				N for Study	73		
14							
15							

8.11 SAMPLE SIZE ESTIMATES FOR TESTS OF PROPORTIONS IN TWO INDEPENDENT SAMPLES

In Chapter 8 of the textbook, we presented a formula to determine the sample size required to ensure adequate power to test the following hypotheses about the difference in proportions in two independent populations:

$$H_0: p_1 = p_2$$

$$H_1: p_1 \neq p_2$$

where p_1 and p_2 are the proportions in the two comparison populations. The formula for determining sample size required in each group to ensure that the test has a specified power is:

$$n_i = 2\left(\frac{z_{1-\alpha/2} + z_{1-\beta}}{\text{ES}}\right)^2$$

where n_i is the sample size required in each group ($i = 1,2$), α is the selected level of significance, and $z_{1-\alpha/2}$ is the value from the standard normal distribution holding $1-\alpha/2$ below it, $1-\beta$ is the selected power, and $z_{1-\beta}$ is the value from the standard normal distribution holding $1-\beta$ below it. ES is the effect size, defined as:

$$ES = \frac{|p_1 - p_2|}{\sqrt{p(1-p)}}$$

where $|p_1 - p_2|$ is the absolute value of the difference in proportions between the two groups expected under the alternative hypothesis, H_1, and p is the overall proportion, based on pooling the data from the two comparison groups. (p can be computed by taking the mean of the proportions in the two comparison groups, assuming that the groups will be of approximately equal size.)

Example 8.10. In Example 8.17 of the textbook, we determined the sample size needed for a clinical trial proposed to evaluate the efficacy of a new drug designed to reduce systolic blood pressure. The primary outcome is diagnosis of hypertension (true/false), defined as a systolic blood pressure above 140 or a diastolic blood pressure above 90. In planning the trial, investigators hypothesized that 30% of the participants would meet the criteria for hypertension in the placebo group and that the new drug would be considered efficacious if there was a 20% reduction in the proportion of patients receiving the new drug who meet the criteria for hypertension (i.e., if the proportion is 24% among patients receiving the new drug). How many patients should be enrolled in the trial to ensure that the power of the test is 80% to detect this difference in the proportions of patients with hypertension? A two-sided test will be used with a 5% level of significance.

We first compute the effect size based on the hypothesized difference in proportions. The proportion expected in the placebo group is entered into cell B1 and the proportion expected in the treatment group is computed as a 20% reduction in B1 using "=B1*(1−0.2)". The data in the Excel worksheet are shown in Figure 8-34.

Before computing the effect size, we need to compute the overall proportion. This is done by taking the mean of the proportions in the two treatment groups using "=(B1+B3)/2". The computation is shown in Figure 8-35. In Figure 8-36, we compute the effect size.

We next enter the level of significance, α, and the desired power to compute $z_{1-\alpha/2}$ and the $z_{1-\beta}$. This is shown in Figure 8-37. The next step is to compute the sample size per group based on the effect size and the appropriate z values for the selected α and power. This is shown in Figure 8-38.

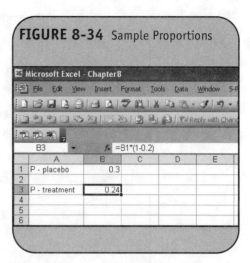

FIGURE 8-34 Sample Proportions

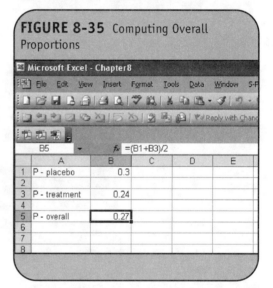

FIGURE 8-35 Computing Overall Proportions

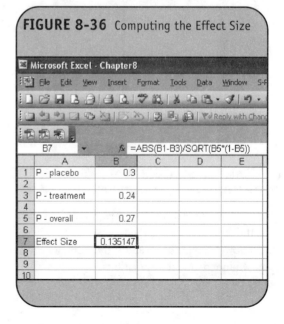

FIGURE 8-36 Computing the Effect Size

Finally, because the sample size formula always produces the minimum number of subjects per group required to ensure that the test has the specified power to detect the desired effect size at the specified level of significance, to determine the numbers of subjects per group required for the study, we must round up. This is done using Excel's ROUNDUP function. The sample sizes required per group are shown in Figure 8-39.

Samples of size $n_1 = 860$ patients on the new drug and $n_2 = 860$ patients on placebo will ensure that the test of hypothesis will have 80% power to detect a 20% reduction in the proportions of patients who meet the criteria for hypertension.

Once the Excel formulas are programmed to compute the sample sizes required to ensure a specified power in a test of

FIGURE 8-37 Computing z Values

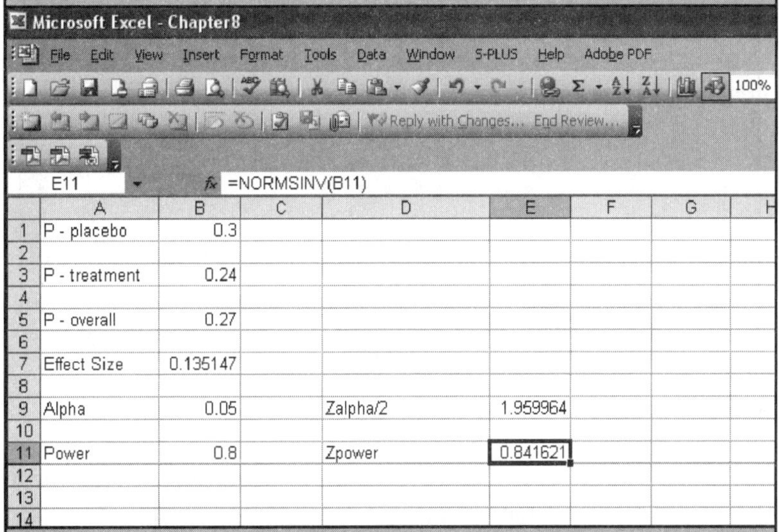

FIGURE 8-38 Determining the Sample Size Required per Group

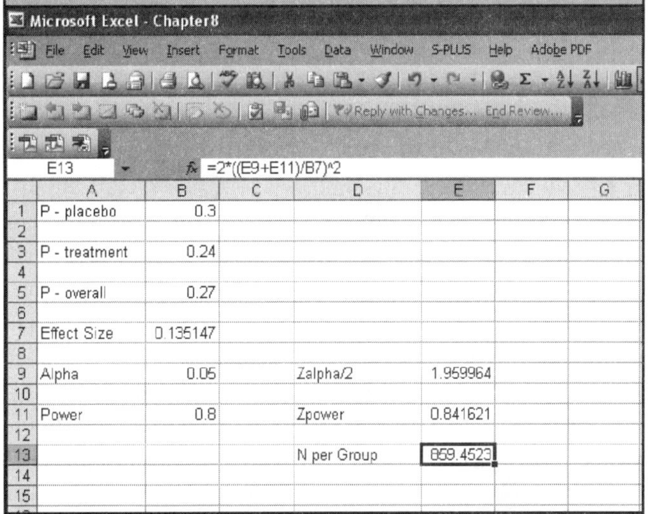

FIGURE 8-39 Sample Size Required per Group for Study

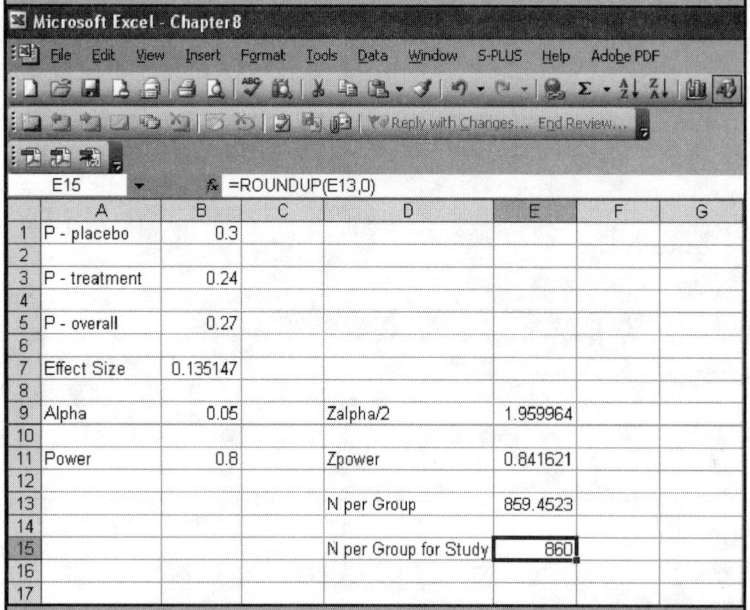

	A	B	C	D	E	F	G
1	P - placebo	0.3					
2							
3	P - treatment	0.24					
4							
5	P - overall	0.27					
6							
7	Effect Size	0.135147					
8							
9	Alpha	0.05		Zalpha/2	1.959964		
10							
11	Power	0.8		Zpower	0.841621		
12							
13				N per Group	859.4523		
14							
15				N per Group for Study	860		
16							
17							

hypothesis, other scenarios can be considered easily by changing the inputs (e.g., α, the desired power, the difference in the parameter reflecting a clinically meaningful change, or the standard deviation).

8.12   PRACTICE PROBLEMS

1. We want to design a new placebo-controlled trial to evaluate an experimental medication to increase lung capacity. The primary outcome is peak expiratory flow rate, a continuous variable measured in liters per minute. The primary outcome will be measured after 6 months on treatment. The expected peak expiratory flow rate in adults is 300 with a standard deviation of 50. How many subjects should be enrolled to ensure 80% power to detect a difference of 15 liters per minute with a two-sided test and $\alpha = 0.05$?

2. An investigator wants to estimate caffeine consumption in high school students. How many students would be required to ensure that a 95% confidence interval estimate for the mean caffeine intake (measured in mg) is within 15 units of the true mean? Assume that the standard deviation in caffeine intake is 68 mg.

3. Consider the study proposed in Problem 2. How many students would be required to estimate the proportion of students who consume coffee? Suppose we want the estimate to be within 5% of the true proportion with 95% confidence.

4. A clinical trial was conducted comparing a new compound designed to improve wound healing in trauma patients to a placebo. After treatment for 5 days, 58% of the patients taking the new compound had a substantial reduction in the size of their wound as compared to 44% in the placebo group. The trial failed to show significance. How many subjects would be required to detect the difference in proportions observed in the trial with 80% power? A two-sided test is planned at $\alpha = 0.05$.

5. A crossover trial is planned to evaluate the impact of an educational intervention program to reduce alcohol consumption in patients determined to be at risk for alcohol problems. The plan is to measure alcohol consumption (the number of drinks on a typical drinking day) before the intervention and then again after participants complete the educational intervention program. How many participants would be

required to ensure that a 95% confidence interval for the mean difference in the number of drinks is within two drinks of the true mean? Assume that the standard deviation of the difference in the mean number of drinks is 6.7 drinks.

6. An investigator wants to design a study to estimate the difference in the proportions of men and women who develop early onset cardiovascular disease (defined as cardiovascular disease before age 50). A study conducted 10 years ago found that 15% and 8% of men and women, respectively, developed early onset cardiovascular disease. How many men and women are needed to generate a 95% confidence interval estimate for the difference in proportions with a margin of error not exceeding 4%?

7. The mean body mass index (BMI) for boys age 12 is 23.6. An investigator wants to test if the BMI is higher in boys age 12 living in New York City. How many boys are needed to ensure that a two-sided test of hypothesis has 80% power to detect an increase in BMI of 2 units? Assume that the standard deviation in BMI is 5.7.

8. An investigator wants to design a study to estimate the difference in the mean BMI between boys and girls age 12 living in New York City. How many boys and girls are needed to ensure that a 95% confidence interval estimate for the difference in mean BMI between boys and girls has a margin of error not exceeding 2 units? Use the estimate of the variability in BMI from Problem 7.

Regression Analysis

In Chapter 9 of the textbook, we introduced regression analysis. We noted that regression analysis is a very general and widely applied technique. In the textbook, we focused more on the use of regression analysis to assess confounding and effect modification. We limit our focus here to estimating simple linear and multiple linear regression models using the linear regression tool in the Data Analysis ToolPak.

We use data collected from $n = 40$ randomly selected participants of the Sixth Examination of the Framingham Offspring Study to illustrate regression analysis using Excel. The data are shown in Table 9-1 and include the participant's age (in years), their gender (which is coded 1 for males and 0 for females), body mass index (BMI), systolic and diastolic blood pressures, total cholesterol, HDL cholesterol, diabetes (coded 1 for participants diagnosed with diabetes and 0 otherwise), and current smoking status (coded 1 for current smokers and 0 otherwise).

9.1 SIMPLE LINEAR REGRESSION ANALYSIS

In Chapter 9 of the textbook, we introduced simple linear regression analysis as a technique for estimating the equation that best describes the linear association between a continuous dependent or outcome variable, y, and a single independent or predictor variable, x. The independent variable can be continuous or dichotomous (sometimes called an indictor variable). The regression equation is:

$$\hat{y} = b_0 + b_1 x$$

where $\hat{y}$ is the estimated value of the dependent or outcome variable, b_0 is the estimated y-intercept, and b_1 is the estimated slope. Excel has an analysis tool that can be used to estimate the y-intercept and slope.

Example 9.1. Suppose we wish to estimate the equation of the line that best describes the relationship between systolic blood pressure (SBP) and age. The data from Table 9-1 are entered into an Excel worksheet as shown in Figure 9-1. Note that the Excel worksheet contains $n = 40$ observations; only the first 20 are shown in Figure 9-1.

To estimate the simple linear regression equation, we use the "Tools/Data Analysis" menu. We select the "Regression Analysis" tool as shown in Figure 9-2 and click "OK." Excel then requests specification of the variables for analysis in the dialog box shown in Figure 9-3.

We first specify the dependent or outcome variable (y). In our example, the dependent variable is systolic blood pressure, which is contained in cell D1 through cell D41. We then specify the independent variable (x), which in this example is age. The age data is contained in cell A1 through cell A41. Because we included the first row (A1 and D1), we click on the "Labels" box to indicate that the labels are contained in these cells. We then specify a location for the results of the regression analysis. For this example, we request that Excel place the results in a new worksheet entitled *Simple Regression*. Excel offers a number of additional details, such as analysis of residuals and normal probability plots. These are used to examine the fit of the regression equation and are called regression diagnostics. (We introduced only the basic applications of regression analysis in the textbook and we restrict our attention to the same in the Excel applications.) The results of the regression analysis are shown in Figure 9-4.

TABLE 9-1 Data from $n = 40$ Randomly Selected Participants of the Sixth Examination of the Framingham Offspring Study

Age	Male	BMI	SBP	DBP	Total Cholesterol	HDL	Diabetes	Smoke
48.2683	1	27.92	140	88	184	35	1	1
47.3347	1	32.61	118	77	178	48	0	1
47.1129	1	34.83	112	69	177	33	0	0
49.0541	1	28.76	128	84	246	54	0	0
45.9548	1	26.76	121	85	193	43	0	0
54.5243	1	27.01	126	77	182	40	0	0
56.2409	1	28.76	124	77	246	50	0	1
52.1068	1	24	131	80	167	40	1	0
56.011	1	30.37	129	81	176	39	1	0
58.2012	1	27.88	121	85	210	45	0	1
51.1129	1	19.67	93	59	174	63	0	0
53.1444	1	25.45	111	79	180	58	0	0
68.8241	1	23.1	151	75	192	31	1	0
66.8611	1	27.44	132	76	180	50	0	1
66.8446	1	29.03	137	56	129	39	0	0
62.152	1	27.25	144	82	216	57	0	0
69.2293	1	24.68	109	75	184	64	0	0
64.3723	1	34.44	133	77	271	50	1	0
61.2567	1	22.86	104	68	198	51	0	0
66.9624	1	27.84	122	60	180	33	1	0
71.7454	1	27.7	137	81	198	44	1	0
71.0089	1	31.04	136	75	213	62	0	0
77.4456	1	34.06	110	57	181	45	0	0
34.6557	0	21.8	99	60	178	33	0	0
59.0773	0	23.59	124	76	212	47	0	0
45.7659	0	22.39	118	77	258	56	0	0
55.9808	0	26.18	110	66	263	50	0	0
47.5729	0	24.86	103	66	183	47	0	0
59.4798	0	32.89	123	85	203	40	0	0
58.3381	0	24.47	118	61	230	81	0	0
50.0589	0	21.98	110	68	168	72	0	1
52.6845	0	25.12	105	67	201	61	0	0
51.7016	0	39.93	131	80	197	43	0	0
58.8255	0	38.14	107	69	224	29	0	0
64.5859	0	25.86	138	68	205	53	0	0
67.0418	0	30.95	135	72	210	36	0	0
62.642	0	31.99	123	65	209	70	0	0
71.8248	0	19.03	103	50	206	63	0	0
76.6899	0	21.8	137	85	176	74	0	0
73.9932	0	33.07	135	80	254	57	0	0

Excel produces a number of statistics and analyses in its standard regression analysis. We will again focus only on the analyses discussed in the textbook. Specifically, the estimates of the regression coefficients are at the end of the results under the column headed *Coefficients*. The estimate of the y-intercept is $b_0 = 89.40$ and the estimate of the slope is $b_1 = 0.56$. (Notice that the slope is the coefficient associated with age.) The regression equation relating age to systolic blood pressure is:

$$\hat{y} = 89.40 + 0.56(\text{Age})$$

where $\hat{y}$ is the estimated SBP. Excel also provides standard errors of the regression coefficients, t statistics, and p-values

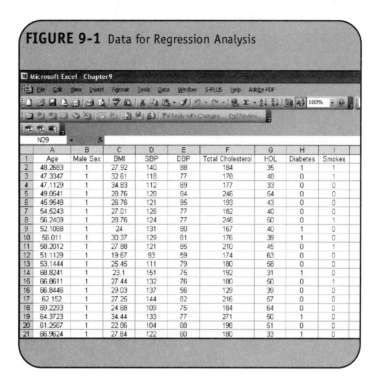

FIGURE 9-1 Data for Regression Analysis

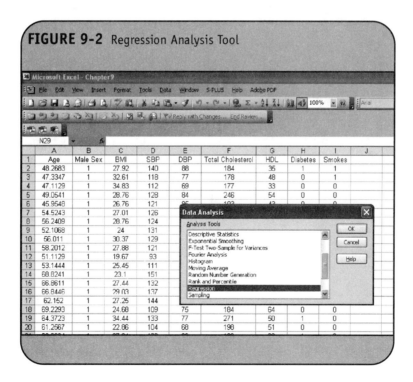

FIGURE 9-2 Regression Analysis Tool

to test whether the statistics are statistically significantly different from zero. Usually, we are not interested in whether the intercept is significantly different from zero. However, it is of interest to test whether the slope is significantly different from zero.

Specifically, we test H_0: $\beta_1 = 0$ versus H_1: $\beta_1 \neq 0$. Excel provides a p-value of 0.0107, indicating that there is a statistically significant association between age and systolic blood pressure. The regression equation indicates that each additional year of age is associated with a 0.56 unit increase in

FIGURE 9-3 Specification of Variables for Simple Linear Regression Analysis

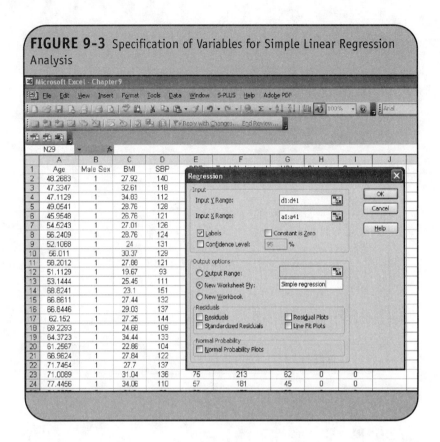

FIGURE 9-4 Results of Simple Linear Regression Analysis

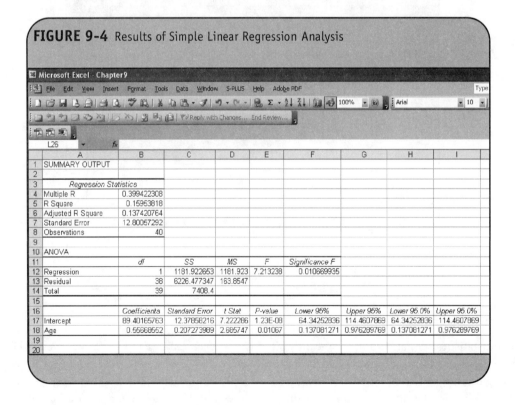

systolic blood pressure. (The other analyses that Excel generates are useful and interested readers should see some of the references at the end of Chapter 9 in the textbook for more details.)

Example 9.2. Suppose we wish to assess whether there is an association between systolic blood pressure and current smoking status using the data in Table 9-1, which were entered into an Excel worksheet as shown in Figure 9-1. We again use the "Tools/Data Analysis" menu and select the "Regression Analysis" tool. When we click "OK," Excel requests specification of the variables for analysis in the dialog box shown in Figure 9-5.

We again specify the dependent or outcome variable (y). In this example, the outcome is systolic blood pressure, which is contained in cell D1 through cell D41. We then specify the independent variable (x), which in this example is smoking. The smoking data is contained in cell I1 through cell I41. Because we included the first row (I1 and D1), we click on the "Labels" box to indicate that the labels are

contained in these cells. We then specify a location for the results of the regression analysis. For this example, we request that Excel place the results in a new worksheet entitled *SBP and Smoking*. The results of the regression analysis are shown in Figure 9-6.

The estimate of the y-intercept is $b_0 = 121.85$ and the estimate of the slope is $b_1 = 2.31$. The regression equation relating current smoking status to systolic blood pressure is:

$$\hat{y} = 121.85 + 2.31(\text{Smoking Status})$$

where $\hat{y}$ is the estimated SBP. The p-value for the test of significance for the slope is $p = 0.7098$, indicating that there is no statistically significant association between current smoking status and systolic blood pressure. The regression equation indicates that smokers have higher systolic blood pressures by approximately 2.31 units, as compared to nonsmokers. However, this difference is not statistically significantly different from zero (because $p = 0.7098$).

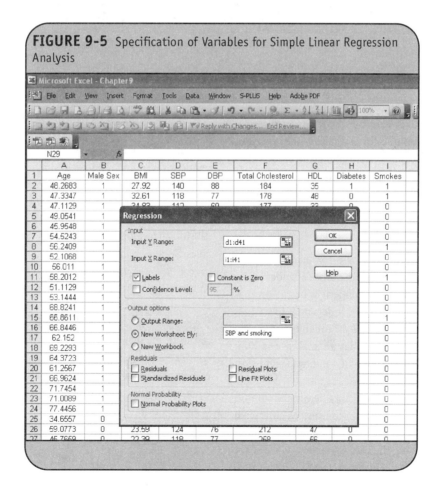

FIGURE 9-5 Specification of Variables for Simple Linear Regression Analysis

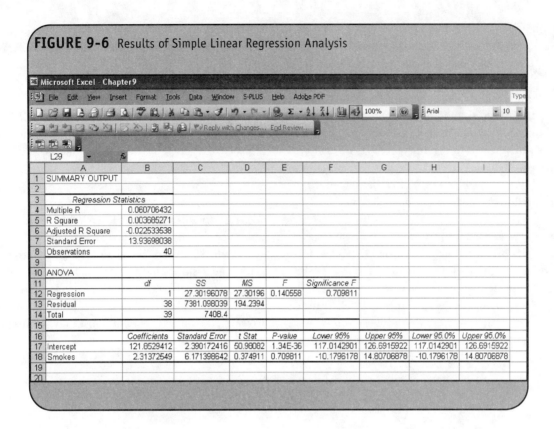

FIGURE 9-6 Results of Simple Linear Regression Analysis

9.2   MULTIPLE LINEAR REGRESSION ANALYSIS

In Chapter 9 of the textbook, we introduced multiple linear regression analysis as a technique for estimating the equation that best describes the association between a continuous outcome variable y and a set of independent variables, $x_1, x_2, ... x_p$. The independent variables can be continuous or dichotomous. The regression equation is:

$$\hat{y} = b_0 + b_1 x_1 + b_2 x_2 + ... + b_p x_p,$$

where $\hat{y}$ is the predicted or expected value of the dependent variable, x_1 through x_p are p distinct independent or predictor variables, b_0 is the value of y when all of the independent variables (x_1 through x_p) are equal to zero, and b_1 through b_p are the estimated regression coefficients. Excel has an analysis tool that can be used to estimate the coefficients of a multiple regression equation.

Example 9.3. Suppose we again consider systolic blood pressure as our dependent or outcome variable. We now wish to assess the association between age and gender, considered simultaneously, on SBP using the data in Table 9-1. We again use the "Tools/Data Analysis" menu and select the "Regression Analysis" tool. When we click "OK," Excel requests specifica-

tion of the variables for analysis in the dialog box shown in Figure 9-7.

We again specify the dependent or outcome variable (y). In Example 9.3, the outcome is systolic blood pressure, which is contained in cell D1 through cell D41. We then specify the independent variables (x_1 and x_2), which in this example are age and gender. The age data is contained in cell A1 through cell A41 and the gender data (in this example, the variable is an indicator of male gender: 1 = male, 0 = female) is contained in cell B1 though cell B41. The range "A1:B41" includes both independent variables. Because we included the first row (A1, B1 and D1) we click on the "Labels" box to indicate that the labels are contained in these cells. We then specify a location for the results of the regression analysis. For this example, we request that Excel place the results in a new worksheet entitled *Multiple Regression*. The results of the regression analysis are shown in Figure 9-8.

The estimate of the coefficients of the multiple regression equation are: $b_0 = 87.19$, $b_1 = 0.54$ and $b_p = 5.38$. The regression equation relating age and gender to systolic blood pressure is:

$$\hat{y} = 87.19 + 0.54(\text{Age}) + 5.38(\text{Gender})$$

where $\hat{y}$ is the estimated SBP. The p-values for the tests of significance for the regression coefficients associated with

FIGURE 9-7 Specification of Variables for Multiple Linear Regression Analysis

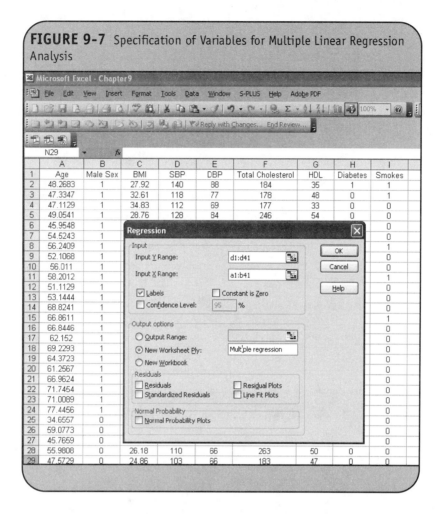

FIGURE 9-8 Results of Multiple Linear Regression Analysis

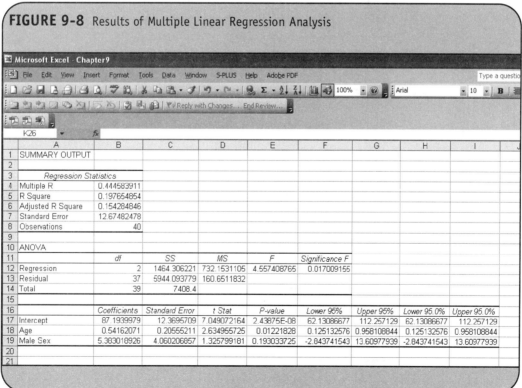

age and gender are $p = 0.0122$ and $p = 0.1930$, respectively. The p-values indicate that there is a statistically significant association between age and systolic blood pressure accounting for gender, but not between gender and systolic blood pressure, once age is considered. The multiple regression equation indicates that each additional year of age is associated with a 0.54 unit increase in systolic blood pressure, holding gender constant, and that men have higher systolic blood pressures than women by about 5.38 units, holding age constant.

Example 9.4. We now consider HDL as our dependent or outcome variable and want to assess the association between BMI and gender, considered simultaneously, on HDL using the data in Table 9-1. We again use the "Tools/Data Analysis" menu and select the "Regression Analysis" tool. When we click "OK," Excel requests specification of the variables for analysis in the dialog box shown in Figure 9-9.

We first specify the location of the data for our dependent or outcome variable (y). In this example, the outcome is HDL, which is contained in cell G1 through cell G41. We then specify the independent variables (x_1 and x_2), which in this example are gender and BMI. The gender data is contained in cell B1 through cell B41 and the BMI data is contained in cell C1 though cell C41. The range "B1:C41" includes both independent variables. Because we included the first row (B1, C1, and G1) we click on the "Labels" box to indicate that the labels are contained in these cells. We then specify a location for the results of the regression analysis. For this example, we request that Excel place the results in a new worksheet entitled *Multiple Regression 2*. The results of the regression analysis are shown in Figure 9-10.

The estimate of the coefficients of the multiple regression equation are as follows: $b_0 = 79.38$, $b_1 = -6.31$, and $b_2 = -0.94$. The regression equation relating gender and BMI to HDL is:

$$\hat{y} = 79.38 - 6.31(\text{Gender}) - 0.94(\text{BMI})$$

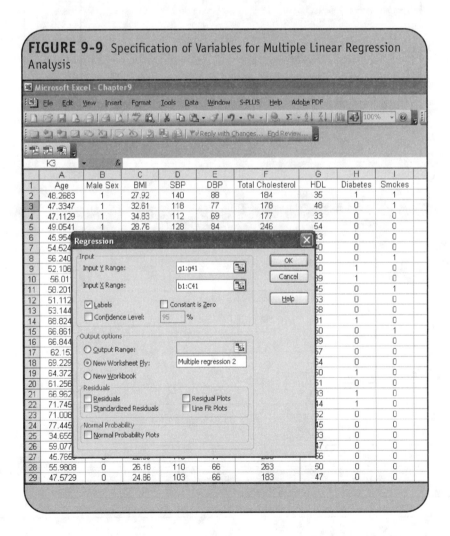

FIGURE 9-9 Specification of Variables for Multiple Linear Regression Analysis

FIGURE 9-10 Results of Multiple Linear Regression Analysis

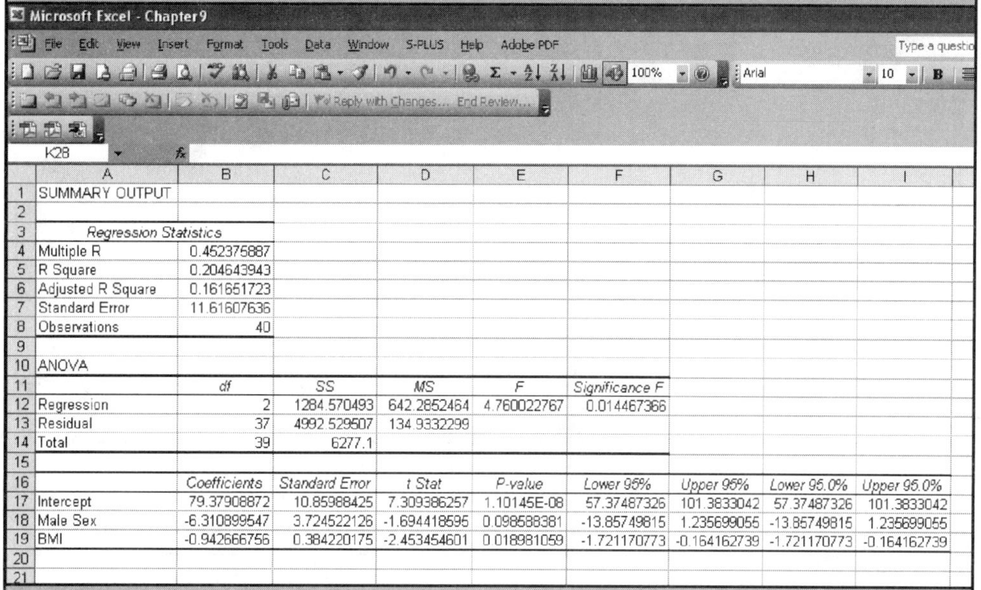

	A	B	C	D	E	F	G	H	I
1	SUMMARY OUTPUT								
2									
3	*Regression Statistics*								
4	Multiple R	0.452375887							
5	R Square	0.204643943							
6	Adjusted R Square	0.161651723							
7	Standard Error	11.61607636							
8	Observations	40							
9									
10	ANOVA								
11		*df*	*SS*	*MS*	*F*	*Significance F*			
12	Regression	2	1284.570493	642.2852464	4.760022767	0.014467366			
13	Residual	37	4992.529507	134.9332299					
14	Total	39	6277.1						
15									
16		*Coefficients*	*Standard Error*	*t Stat*	*P-value*	*Lower 95%*	*Upper 95%*	*Lower 95.0%*	*Upper 95.0%*
17	Intercept	79.37908872	10.85988425	7.309386257	1.10145E-08	57.37487326	101.3833042	57.37487326	101.3833042
18	Male Sex	-6.310899547	3.724522126	-1.694418595	0.098588381	-13.85749815	1.235699055	-13.85749815	1.235699055
19	BMI	-0.942666756	0.384220175	-2.453454601	0.018981059	-1.721170773	-0.164162739	-1.721170773	-0.164162739
20									
21									

where $\hat{y}$ is the estimated HDL. The p-values for the tests of significance for the regression coefficients associated with gender and BMI are $p = 0.0986$ and $p = 0.0190$, respectively. The p-values indicate that there is a marginally significant association between gender and HDL (often when p-values fall in the range of 0.05 to 0.10, they are described as marginally significant), accounting for BMI, and a statistically significant association between BMI and HDL, accounting for gender. The multiple regression equation indicates that men have lower HDL than women by about 6.31 units, holding BMI constant, and that each additional unit of BMI is associated with a 0.94 unit reduction in HDL. Recall that HDL is the "good cholesterol" and that higher values are better. Thus, increased BMI is associated with decreased HDL.

It is important to note that for multiple regression analysis, the independent or predictor variables ($x_1, x_2, x_3, \ldots, x_p$) must be in adjacent columns in the Excel worksheet. When we specify the location of the cells containing the independent variables (i.e., Input x Range, Figure 9-9), we specify the locations of the first and last cells in the adjacent columns containing the data. For example, suppose in Example 9.3 we wished to consider gender and diabetes as the independent variables. To use the Regression Analysis Tool (to correctly specify these independent variables), we would need to reorganize the data in the Excel worksheet so that gender and diabetes were in adjacent columns. This can be done in several different ways. An easy way is to copy the data from column B and column H into column K and column L, as shown in Figure 9-11.

To estimate the multiple regression equation, we use the "Tools/Data Analysis" menu and select the "Regression Analysis" tool. When we click "OK," Excel requests specification of the variables for analysis in the dialog box shown in Figure 9-12.

We again specify the location of the data for our dependent or outcome variable (y = HDL), which is contained in cell G1 through cell G41. We then specify the independent variables (x_1 and x_2, or gender and diabetes), which are now contained in cell K1 through cell L41. The analysis is performed as described in Example 9.3 and Example 9.4.

9.3 PRACTICE PROBLEMS

1. Consider the data shown in Table 9-2 measured in a sample of $n = 25$ undergraduates in an on-campus survey of health behaviors. Enter the data into an Excel worksheet for analysis.

FIGURE 9-11 Organizing the Data for a Multiple Regression Analysis

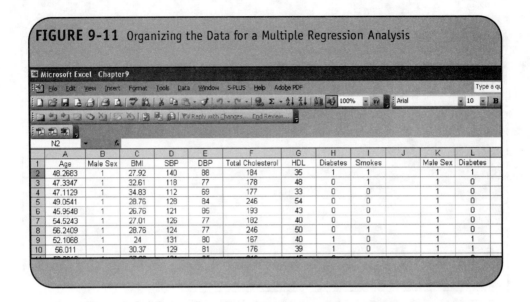

FIGURE 9-12 Specification of Variables for Multiple Linear Regression Analysis

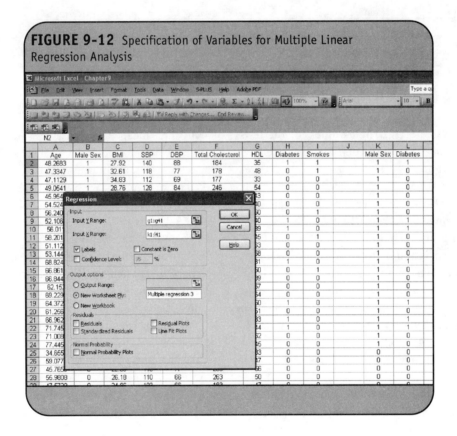

TABLE 9-2 Data for Practice Problems

ID	Age	Female	Year in School	GPA	Current Smoker	Exercise per Week (h)	Average Drinks per Week	Cups of Coffee per Week
1	18	1	Fr	3.85	1	7	3	3
2	21	0	Jr	3.27	1	3	2	4
3	19	1	So	2.90	0	0	4	7
4	22	0	Sr	3.65	1	0	2	4
5	21	1	Sr	3.41	1	0	1	3
6	20	0	Jr	3.20	0	2	5	8
7	19	1	Jr	2.89	1	1	4	10
8	17	0	Fr	3.75	0	6	0	0
9	18	0	So	4.00	0	6	2	6
10	17	1	So	3.18	0	3	5	7
11	21	0	Jr	2.58	1	3	12	12
12	22	1	Sr	2.98	0	2	3	4
13	19	0	Fr	3.16	1	2	0	6
14	21	1	Jr	3.36	1	3	1	2
15	22	1	So	3.72	0	6	3	0
16	19	0	So	3.30	1	4	0	6
17	16	0	Fr	3.28	0	4	0	5
18	22	0	Sr	2.98	0	0	8	5
19	17	1	Fr	3.90	0	7	0	2
20	20	1	Sr	3.78	1	4	6	2
21	21	1	So	3.26	1	2	3	4
22	23	0	Jr	3.01	0	1	9	7
23	23	0	Sr	3.83	1	5	4	4
24	17	1	Fr	3.76	0	5	2	1
25	22	1	Sr	3.05	0	1	5	5

2. Estimate the simple linear regression equation relating number of cups of coffee per week to GPA (consider GPA the dependent or outcome variable).

3. Estimate the simple linear regression equation relating female gender to GPA (consider GPA the dependent or outcome variable).

4. Estimate the multiple linear regression equation relating number of cups of coffee per week, female gender, and number of hours of exercise per week to GPA (consider GPA the dependent or outcome variable).